It's another Quality Book from CGP

This book is for anyone doing AQA Modular GCSE Mathematics at Intermediate Level.

Whatever subject you're doing it's the same old story — there are lots of facts and you've just got to learn them. KS4 Maths is no different.

Happily this CGP book gives you all that important information as clearly and concisely as possible.

It's also got some daft bits in to try and make the whole experience at least vaguely entertaining for you.

What CGP is all about

Our sole aim here at CGP is to produce the highest quality books — carefully written, immaculately presented and dangerously close to being funny.

Then we work our socks off to get them out to you — at the cheapest possible prices.

Contents

Don't panic! We haven't forgotten about Modules Two and Four — they're coursework modules, so you don't need to revise them for the exams.

Published by Coordination Group Publications Ltd.
Written by Richard Parsons
Design Editor: Ruso Bradley
Updated by: Tim Major, Mark Moody, Julie Schofield

ISBN 1 84146 004 4
Groovy website: www.cgpbooks.co.uk
With thanks to Michael Clarke for the proofreading.
Printed by Elanders Hindson, Newcastle upon Tyne.

Probability

This is nobody's favourite subject — for sure, I've never really spoken to anyone who's said they do like it (not for long anyway).
Although it does seem a bit of a "Black Art" to most people, it's not as bad as you might think, but YOU MUST LEARN THE BASIC FACTS, which is what we have on these 2 pages.

All Probabilities are between 0 and 1

A probability of ZERO means it will NEVER HAPPEN,
A probability of ONE means it DEFINITELY WILL.

You can't have a probability bigger than 1.

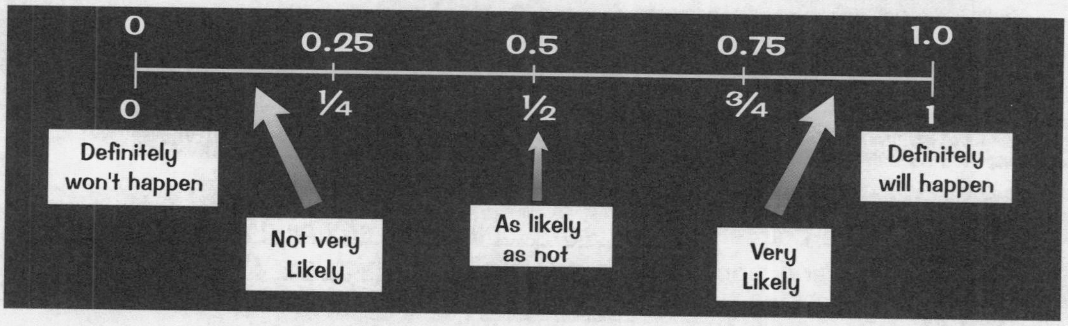

You should be able to put the probability of any event happening on this scale of 0 to 1.

Three Important Details

1) PROBABILITIES SHOULD BE GIVEN as either A FRACTION (¼), or A DECIMAL (0.25) or A PERCENTAGE (25%)
2) THE NOTATION : "P(x) = ½" SHOULD BE READ AS: "The probability of event X happening is ½"
3) PROBABILITIES ALWAYS ADD UP TO 1. This is essential for finding the probability of *the other outcome.* e.g. If P(pass) = ¼, then P(fail) = ¾

THREE IMPORTANT EXTRAS

1) USE YOUR CALCULATOR FRACTION BUTTON $a^{b}/_{c}$ *whenever you can* for multiplying or adding fractions.
2) Watch out for "WITH REPLACEMENT" and "WITHOUT REPLACEMENT" and make sure you know what difference it makes.
(Either you put the thing back after the first go, before having your second go, or you don't — the 2nd tree diagram on P.3 illustrates what can happen)
3) The COMBINED PROBABILITY of two events BOTH happening is ALWAYS LESS than the probability of either of them occurring alone.

The Acid Test:

LEARN the diagram and the 6 IMPORTANT POINTS on this page. Then turn over and write it all down.

1) If P(picking a blue ball) is ¼, what is the value of P(not picking a blue ball)?

Probability

1) Unequal Probabilities You Can Work Out

These make for more interesting questions. (Which means you'll get them in the Exam.)

EXAMPLE 1: *"A bag contains 6 blue balls, 5 red balls and 9 green balls. Find the probability of picking out a green ball."*

ANSWER: The chances of picking out the three colours are NOT EQUAL.
The probability of picking a green is simply:

$$\frac{\text{NUMBER OF GREENS}}{\text{TOTAL NUMBER OF BALLS}} = \frac{9}{20}$$

EXAMPLE 2: *"What is the probability of winning £45 on this spinner?"*

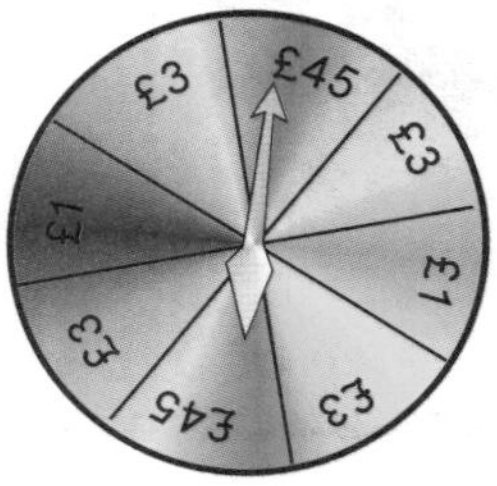

ANSWER:
The pointer has *the same chance of stopping on every sector*...
... and since there are *2 out of 8 which are £45*
then it's a *2 out of 8 chance* of getting £45.

BUT REMEMBER ... you have to say this as a FRACTION or a DECIMAL or a PERCENTAGE:

2 out of 8 is 2 ÷ 8 which is 0.25 (as a decimal)
or ¼ (as a fraction) or 25% (as a percentage)

2) The Probability of the OPPOSITE Happening is just the rest of the probability that's left over

This is simple enough AS LONG AS YOU REMEMBER IT.
If the probability of something happening is say 0.3 then the chance of it NOT HAPPENING is just the rest of the probability that's left over.

Example: A loaded dice has a 0.25 chance of coming up TWO.
What is the chance of it *not* coming up TWO?

Answer: $1 - 0.25 = 0.75$
So, the chance of the dice *not* coming up TWO is 0.75

3) Listing All Outcomes: 2 Coins, Dice, Spinners

A simple question you might get is to list all the possible results from tossing two coins or two spinners or a dice and a spinner, etc.
Whatever it is, it'll be very similar to these, so LEARN THEM:

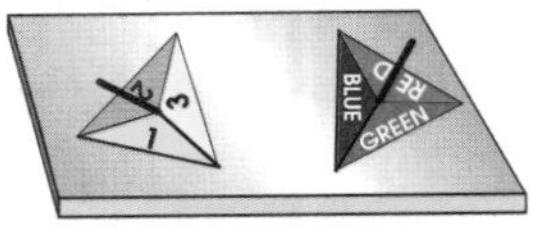

The *possible outcomes* from TOSSING TWO COINS are:

Head	Head	H H
Head	Tail	H T
Tail	Head	T H
Tail	Tail	T T

From TWO SPINNERS with 3 sides:

BLUE + 1	RED + 1	GREEN + 1
BLUE + 2	RED + 2	GREEN + 2
BLUE + 3	RED + 3	GREEN + 3

Try and list the possible outcomes METHODICALLY — to make sure you get them ALL.

Probability — Tree Diagrams

General Tree Diagram

Tree Diagrams are all pretty much the same, so it's a pretty darned good idea to learn these basic details (which apply to ALL tree diagrams) — ready for the one in the Exam.

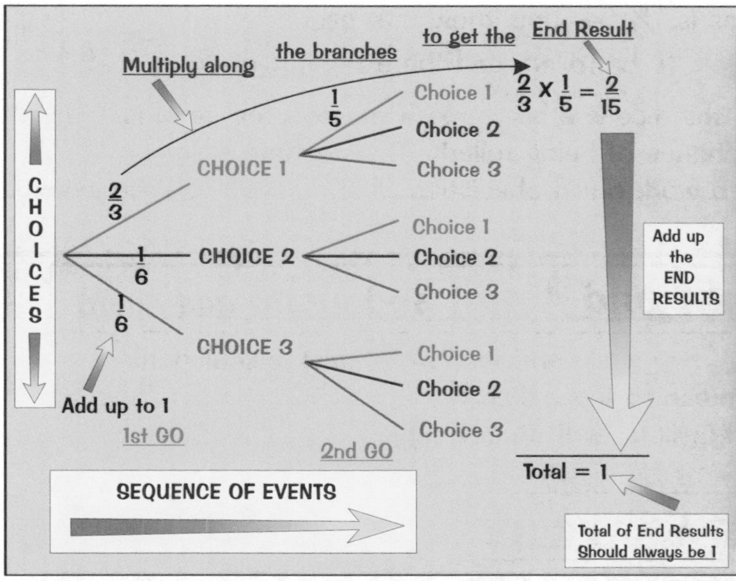

1) *Always MULTIPLY ALONG THE BRANCHES* (as shown) to get the END RESULTS.
2) *On any set of branches which all meet at a point*, the numbers must always ADD UP TO 1.
3) *Check that your diagram is correct* by making sure the End Results ADD UP TO ONE.
4) *To answer any question*, simply ADD UP THE RELEVANT END RESULTS (see below).

A likely Tree Diagram Question

EXAMPLE: "A box contains 5 red disks and 3 green disks. Two disks are taken without replacement. Draw a tree diagram and hence find the probability that both disks are the same colour."

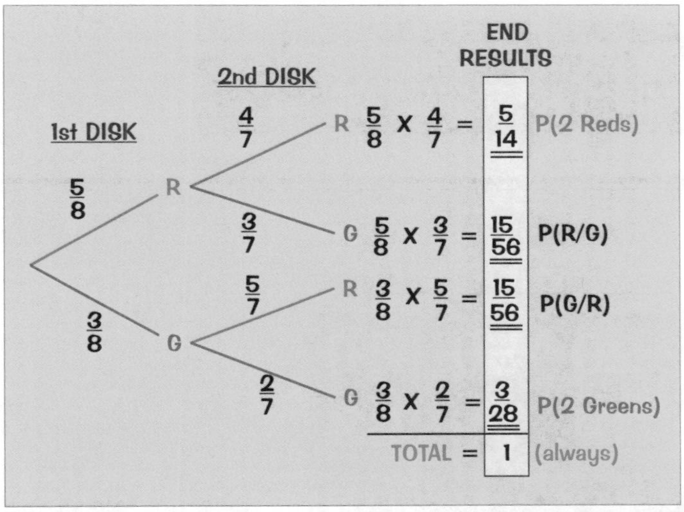

Once the tree diagram is drawn all you then need to do to answer the question is simply select the RELEVANT END RESULTS and then ADD THEM TOGETHER:

2 REDS (5/14)
2 GREENS (3/28)

$$\frac{5}{14} + \frac{3}{28} = \frac{13}{28}$$

If you can, use a calculator for this. Otherwise, use the fraction rules on P.24.

The Acid Test:

LEARN the GENERAL DIAGRAM for Tree Diagrams and the 4 points that go with them.

1) O.K. let's see what you've learnt shall we:
   TURN OVER AND WRITE DOWN EVERYTHING YOU KNOW ABOUT TREE DIAGRAMS.
2) A bag contains 6 red tarantulas and 4 black tarantulas. If two girls each pluck out a tarantula at random without replacement, draw a tree diagram to find the probability that they get different coloured ones.

Relative Frequency

This isn't the number of times your granny comes to visit.
It's a way of working out probabilities.

Fair or Biased?

The probability of rolling a three on a dice is $\frac{1}{6}$ — you know that each of the 6 numbers on a dice is equally likely to be rolled, and there's only 1 three.

BUT this only works if it's a fair dice. If the dice is a bit wonky (the technical term is "biased") then each number won't have an equal chance of being rolled. That's where Relative Frequency comes in — you can use it to work out probabilities when things might be wonky.

Do the Experiment Again and Again and Again and Again

You need to do an experiment over and over again and then do a quick calculation.
(Remember, an experiment could just mean rolling a dice.)
Usually the results of these experiments will be written in a table.

The Formula for Relative Frequency

$$\text{Probability of something happening} = \frac{\text{Number of times it has happened}}{\text{Number of times you tried}}$$

You can work out the relative frequency as a fraction but usually decimals are best.

The important thing to remember is:

The more times you do the experiment, the more accurate the probability will be.

Example:

So, back to the wonky dice. What is the probability of rolling a three?

Number of Times the dice was rolled	10	20	50	100
Number of threes rolled	2	5	11	23
Relative frequency	$\frac{2}{10}=0.2$	$\frac{5}{20}=0.25$	$\frac{11}{50}=0.22$	$\frac{23}{100}=0.23$

So, what's the probability? We've got 4 possible answers, but the best is the one worked out using the highest number of dice rolls.
This makes the probability of rolling a three on this dice 0.23.

And since for a fair, unbiased dice, the probability of rolling a three is $\frac{1}{6}$ (about 0.17), then our dice is biased.

Graphs and Charts

Make sure you know all these easy details:

1) Line Graphs or "Frequency Polygons"

A line graph or "frequency polygon" is just a set of points joined up with straight lines.

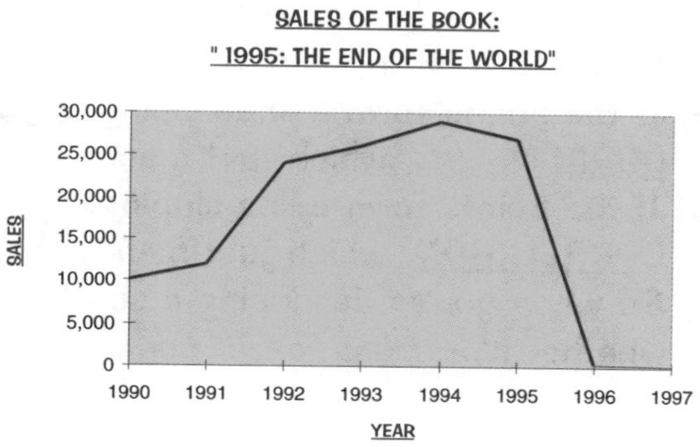

2) Two-Way Tables

Two-way tables are a bit like frequency tables (see P.10), but they show two different things instead of just one. They're pretty straightforward — but you don't want to make any silly mistakes, so listen up.

EXAMPLE:

"Use this table to work out how many
(a) right-handed people and
(b) left-handed women there were in this survey."

	Women	Men	TOTAL
Left-handed		27	63
Right-handed	164	173	
TOTAL	200	200	400

ANSWER:

(a) Either: (i) *add up* the number of right-handed women and the number of right-handed men. So that's 164 + 173 = *337 right-handed people*.

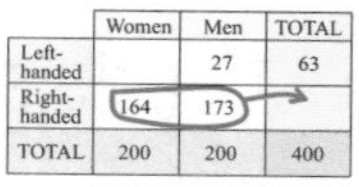

Or: (ii) *take away* the total number of left-handed people from the total number of people. So that's 400 – 63 = *337 right-handed people*.

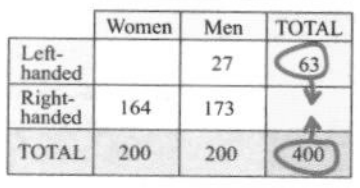

(b) Either: (i) take away the number of right-handed women from the total number of women. That's 200 – 164 = *36 left-handed women*.

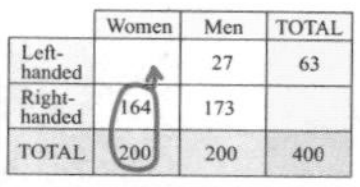

Or: (ii) take away the left-handed men from the total number of left-handed people. Which would be 63 – 27 = *36 left-handed women*.

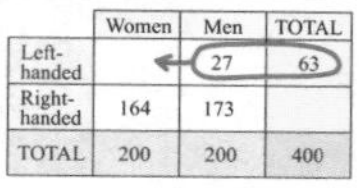

3) Scatter Graphs

1) A SCATTER GRAPH is just a load of points on a graph that *end up in a bit of a mess* rather than in a nice line or curve.
2) There's a fancy word to say how much of a mess they're in — it's CORRELATION.
3) *Good Correlation* (or *Strong* Correlation) means the points *form quite a nice line (the line of best fit)*, and it means *the two things are closely related to each other*.

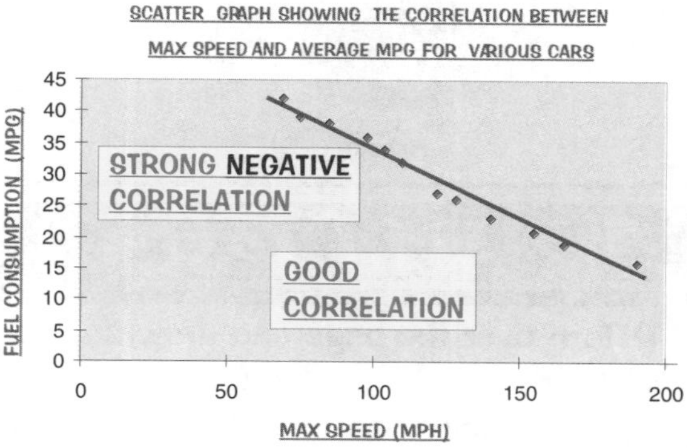

Graphs and Charts

Scatter Graphs (continued)

4) Poor Correlation (or *Weak* Correlation) means the points are all over the place and so there's very little relation between the two things.
5) If the points form a line sloping UPHILL from left to right, then there is POSITIVE CORRELATION, which just means that both things increase or decrease together.
6) If the points form a line sloping DOWNHILL from left to right, then there is NEGATIVE CORRELATION, which just means that as one thing increases the other decreases.
7) So when you're describing a scatter graph you have to mention both things, i.e. whether it's strong/weak/moderate correlation *and* whether it's positive/negative.

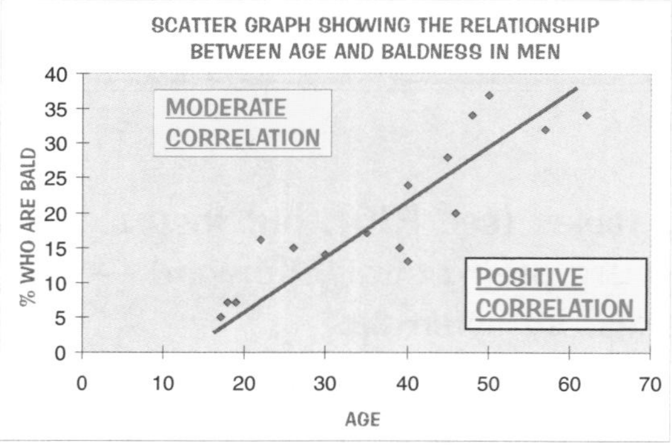

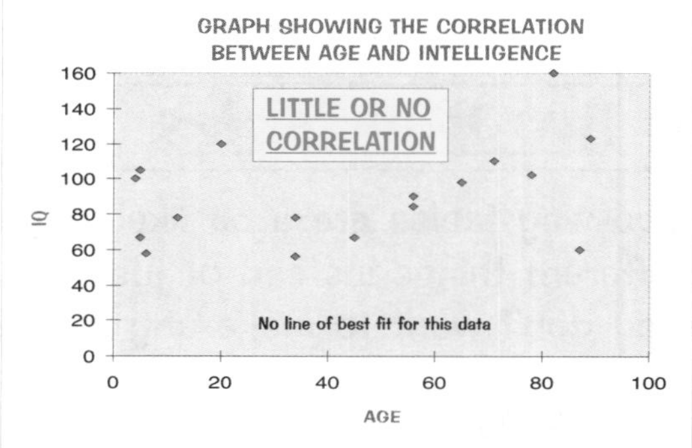

4) Pie Charts

Learn the Golden Rule for Pie Charts:

The TOTAL of Everything = 360°

Creature	Stick insects	Hamsters	Guinea Pigs	Rabbits	Ducks	Total
Number	12	20	17	15	26	90
		×4				×4
Angle		80°				360°

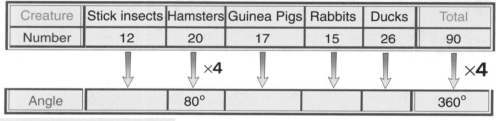

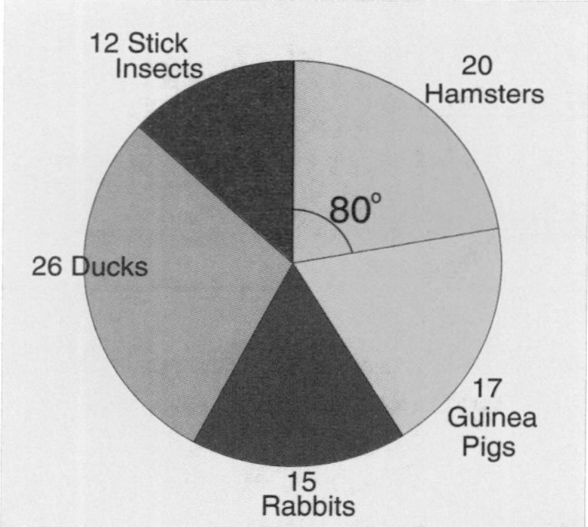

1) Add up all the numbers in each sector to get the TOTAL (←90 for this one).
2) Then find the MULTIPLIER (or divider) that you need to turn your total into 360°:
   For 90 →360 as above, the MULTIPLIER is 4.
3) Now MULTIPLY EVERY NUMBER BY 4 to get the angle for each sector.
   E.g. the angle for hamsters will be $20 \times 4 = 80°$.

The Acid Test:

LEARN THE NAMES of the four types of CHART.

1) Turn over the page and draw an example of each of the 4 charts.
2) Work out the angles for all the other animals in the pie chart shown above.
3) If the points on a scatter graph are all over the place, what does it tell you about the two things that the scatter graph is comparing?

Stem & Leaf Diagrams and Distribution

Shapes of Distributions are Measures of "Spread"

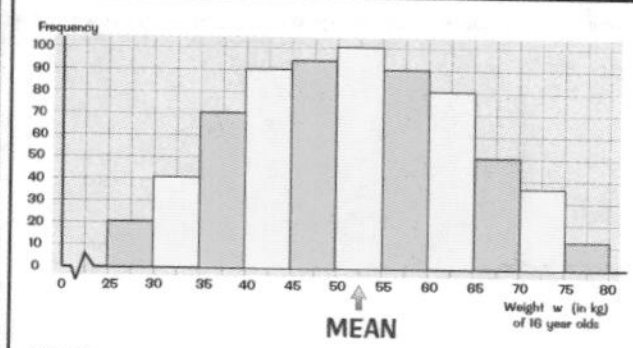

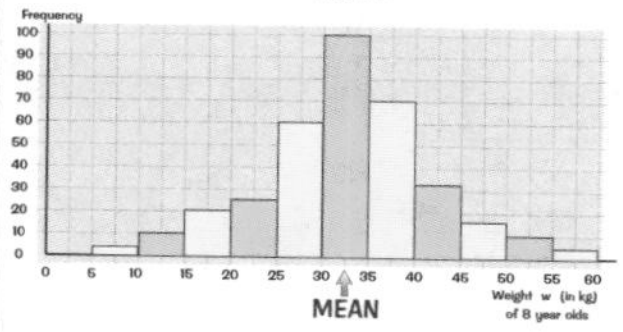

You must LEARN the significance of the shapes of these two histograms:

1) This one shows *high dispersion* i.e. a *large spread* of results away from the mean. (E.g. the weights of a sample of 16 year olds will cover a very wide range.)

2) This second one shows a "*tighter*" distribution of results where most values are within a *narrow range* either side of the mean. (E.g. the weights of a sample of 8 year olds will show very little variation.)

Stem and Leaf diagrams use the actual data

A stem and leaf diagram is a bit like a histogram, but the data itself is used to make the diagram.

This is the stem... ...and these are the leaves.

0	5 6
1	0 1 4 5 7 7 8 8 9
2	1 1 1 2 4 4 6 7 8 9
3	1 4 4 9

Key: 1 | 4 means 14

The *key* tells you *how to read* the diagram. For example, 3 in the stem and 1, 4, 4, and 9 in the leaf represent 31, 34, 34 and 39.

With a stem and leaf diagram, the class widths have to be equal.

You can *choose* the widths of the classes, *but don't be silly* and choose the classes to be 0-30 and 30-60.

0	
5	0 1
10	0 1 4
15	0 2 2 3 3 4
20	1 1 1 2 4 4
25	1 2 3 4
30	1 4 4
35	4

Key: 15 | 3 means 18

Using the key, you can work out that this row of numbers represents 15, 17, 17, 18, 18 and 19...

...and this one represents 31, 34 and 34.

The Bigger the Sample Size, the Better the Estimate

There are FOUR DIFFERENT TYPES OF SAMPLING: (you don't need to know them in any detail)

RANDOM — *this is where you just select individuals "at random".*

SYSTEMATIC — *start with a random selection and select every 10th or 100th one after that.*

STRATIFIED — *where there's different 'layers' to choose from — classes/pupils; departments/employees etc.*

QUOTA — *where the sample reflects the whole population — same ratio of males:females, adults:children etc.*

If you *repeated* any of these experiments, you'd get *different* overall results each time. Likewise...

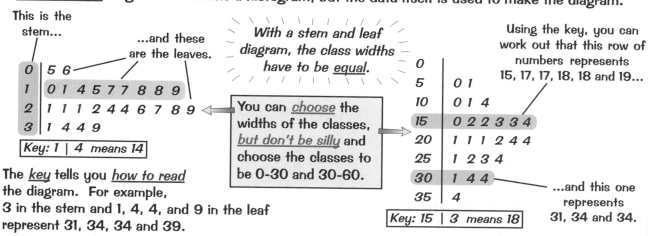

FOR *ANY* SAMPLING METHOD, THE *LARGER* THE *SAMPLE SIZE* (I.E. THE MORE PEOPLE ASKED), THE *BETTER* AN *ESTIMATE* YOU'LL GET OF [THE PARAMETERS FOR] THE *WHOLE POPULATION*.

The Acid Test: LEARN what a stem and leaf diagram is, and how to create your own from some data, and remember this.

1) A survey was done to investigate the average age of cars on Britain's roads by standing on a motorway bridge and noting the registration of the first 200 cars. Give a reason why this is a poor sampling technique and suggest a better approach.

Mean, Median, Mode and Range

Mean, Median and Mode are three types of average: they tell you how big or small the values are in a set of data overall. The Range gives you an idea of how spread out the data is.

Mean, Median, Mode and Range

Example: Here's how to work them out for these numbers
2, 5, 3, 2, 6, -4, 0, 9, -3, 1, 6, 3, -2, 3

1) MEAN $= \frac{\text{total}}{\text{number}} = \frac{-4-3-2+0+1+2+2+3+3+3+5+6+6+9}{14}$
$= 31 \div 14 = \underline{2.21}$

2) MEDIAN = the middle value (only when they're arranged in order of size, that is!).

When there are TWO MIDDLE NUMBERS, as in this case, then the median is HALFWAY BETWEEN THE TWO MIDDLE NUMBERS

-4, -3, -2, 0, 1, 2, [2, 3], 3, 3, 5, 6, 6, 9
← seven numbers this side ↑ seven numbers this side →
Median = (2 + 3) ÷ 2 = 2.5

3) MODE = most common value, which is simply 3. (Or you can say "The modal value is 3")

4) RANGE = distance from lowest to highest value, i.e. from -4 up to 9, = 13

Comparing Two Sets of Data

To compare data, always talk about two things:

1) Mean — this tells you wish set of data has the biggest values overall.

2) Range — this tells you which set of data is more spread out.

Example:

	Mean	Range
Class A	47	24
Class B	53	32

Class B's mean was higher. That means they did better overall in the test.

Class A had a smaller range, meaning that their scores were closer together (they were more consistent).

The Acid Test: LEARN The Four Definitions...

..then cover this page and write them down from memory.

1) Apply all that you have learnt to find the mean, median, mode and range for this set of data: 1, 3, 14, -5, 6, -12, 18, 7, 23, 10, -5, -14, 0, 25, 8

Time Series

Time Series — Measure the Same Thing over a Period of Time

A time series is what you get if you measure the same thing at a number of different times.

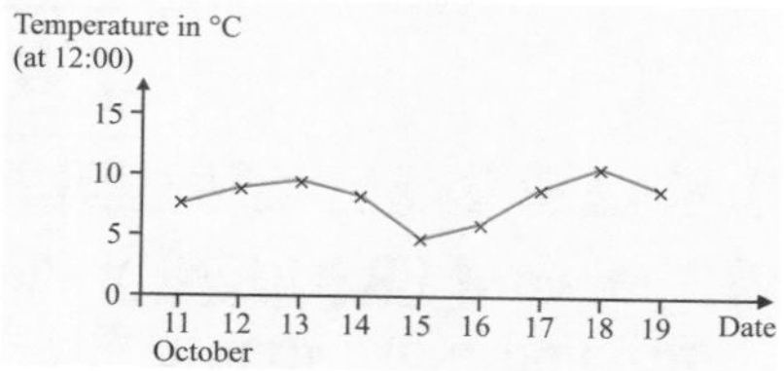

EXAMPLE: Measuring the temperature in your greenhouse at 12 o'clock each day gives you a time series — other examples might be profit figures, crime figures or rainfall.

__THE RETAIL PRICE INDEX (RPI) IS A TIME SERIES:__ Every month, the prices of loads of items (same ones each month) — are combined to get an index number called the RPI, which is a kind of average. As goods get more expensive, this index number gets higher and higher. So when you see on TV that inflation this month is 2.5%, what it actually means is that the RPI is increasing at an annual rate of 2.5%.

Seasonality — The Same Basic Pattern

This is when there's a definite pattern that REPEATS ITSELF every so often. This is called SEASONALITY and the "so often" is called the PERIOD.

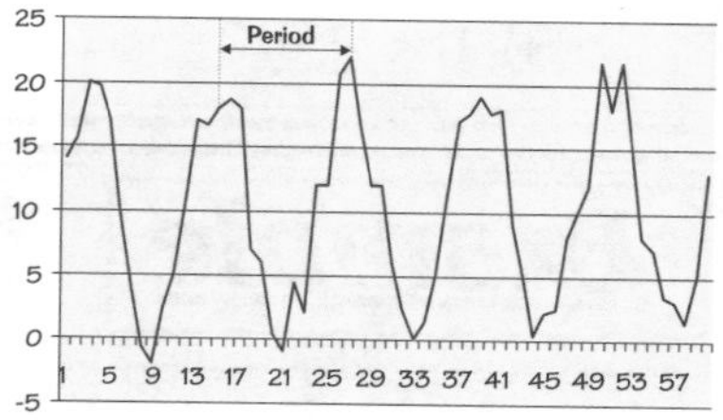

To find the PERIOD, measure PEAK TO PEAK (or trough to trough).

This series has a period of 12 months. There are a few irregularities, so the pattern isn't exactly the same every 12 months, but it's about right.

Trend — Ignoring the Wrinkles

This time series has lots of random fluctuations but there's a definite upwards trend.

The pink line is the trend line.
It's straight, so this is a linear trend.

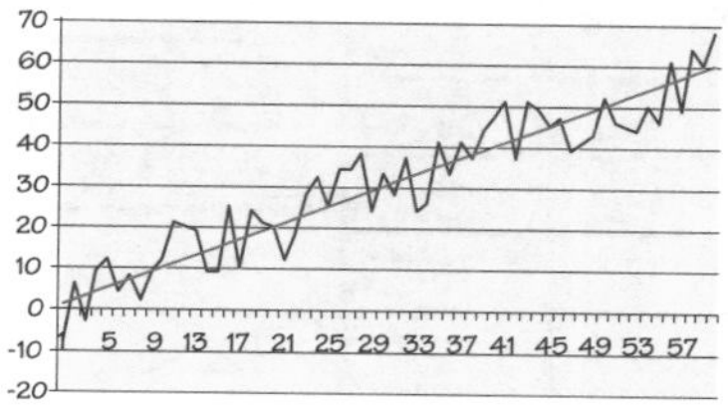

Moving Average — Smooths Out the Seasonality

It's easier to spot a trend if you can 'get rid of' the seasonality and some of the irregularities.

One way to smooth the series is to use a moving average.

This is a time series that definitely looks periodic — but it's difficult to tell if there's a trend.

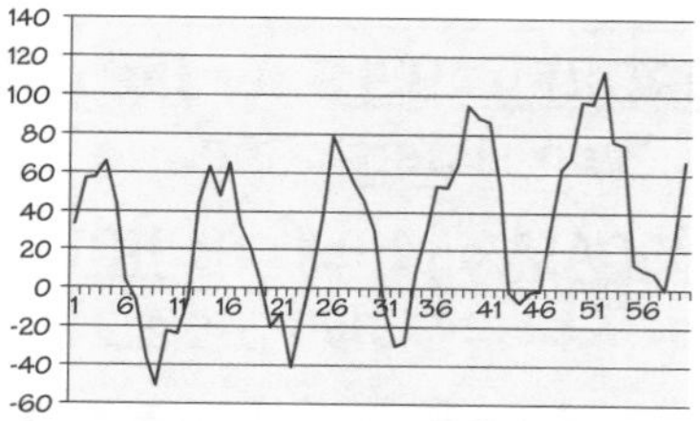

... but plot the moving average
(in pink — must be pink — that's dead important)...

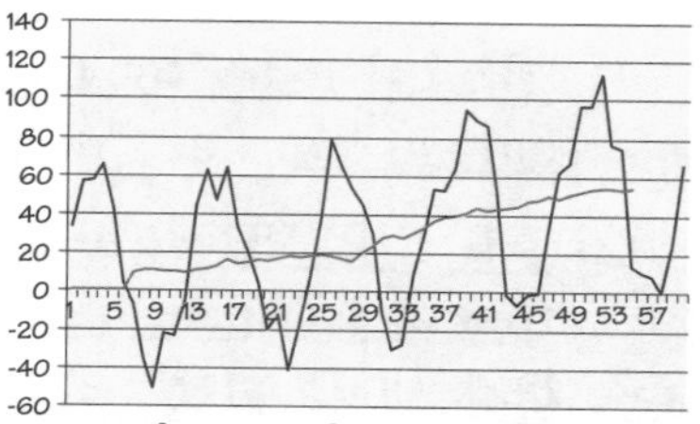

The period is 12, so you use 12 values for the moving average:

...and you can easily see the upward trend.

HOW TO FIND A MOVING AVERAGE:

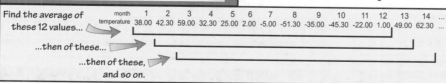

month	1	2	3	4	5	6	7	8	9	10	11	12	13	14	...
temperature	38.00	42.30	59.00	32.30	25.00	2.00	-5.00	-51.30	-35.00	-45.30	-22.00	1.00	49.00	62.30	...

Find the average of these 12 values... (months 1–12)
...then of these... (months 2–13)
...then of these, and so on. (months 3–14)

The Acid Test:

LEARN the words TIME SERIES, SEASONALITY, PERIOD, TREND, MOVING AVERAGE. Cover the page and write a description of each.

1) My town's rainfall is measured every month for 20 yrs and graphed. There's a rough pattern, which repeats itself every 4 months. a) What is the period of this time series? b) Describe how to calculate a moving average.

Frequency Tables

Frequency Tables can either be done in rows or in columns of numbers and they can be quite confusing, but not if you learn these Eight key points:

Eight Key Points

1) ALL FREQUENCY TABLES ARE THE SAME.
2) The word FREQUENCY just means HOW MANY, so a frequency table is nothing more than a "How many in each group" table.
3) The FIRST ROW (or column) just gives the GROUP LABELS.
4) The SECOND ROW (or column) gives the ACTUAL DATA.
5) You have to WORK OUT A THIRD ROW (or column) yourself.
6) The MEAN is always found using: **3rd Row total ÷ 2nd Row Total.**
7) The MEDIAN is found from the MIDDLE VALUE in the 2nd row.
8) The RANGE is found from the EXTREMES of the first row.

Example

Here is a typical frequency table shown in both ROW FORM and COLUMN FORM:

No. of Sisters	Frequency	No. x Frequency
0	7	0
1	15	15
2	12	24
3	8	24
4	3	12
5	1	5
6	0	0
TOTALS	46	80
	(People asked)	(Sisters)

Column Form

No. of sisters	0	1	2	3	4	5	6	totals	
Frequency	7	15	12	8	3	1	0	46	(People asked)
No. x Frequency	0	15	24	24	12	5	0	80	(Sisters)

Row form

There's no real difference between these two forms and you could get either one in your Exam. Whichever you get, make sure you remember these THREE IMPORTANT FACTS:

1) THE 1ST ROW (or column) gives us the GROUP LABELS for the different categories: i.e. "no sisters", "one sister", "two sisters", etc.
2) THE 2ND ROW (or column) is the ACTUAL DATA and tells us HOW MANY (people) THERE ARE in each category i.e. 7 people had "no sisters", 15 people had "one sister", etc.
3) THE THIRD ROW (or column) is ALWAYS obtained by MULTIPLYING the numbers FROM THE FIRST 2 ROWS (or columns).

THIRD ROW = 1ST ROW × 2ND ROW

The Acid Test:

LEARN the 8 RULES for Frequency Tables, then turn over and WRITE THEM DOWN to see what you know.

Using this frequency table, find the MEAN, MEDIAN, MODE and RANGE of the no. of phones that people have.

No. of Phones	0	1	2	3	4	5	6
Frequency	1	25	53	34	22	5	1

Grouped Frequency Tables

These are a bit trickier than simple frequency tables, but they can still look deceptively simple, like this one which shows the distribution of weights of a bunch of 60 school kids.

Weight (kg)	31 — 40	41 — 50	51 — 60	61 — 70	71 — 80
Frequency	8	16	18	12	6

Class Boundaries and Mid-Interval Values

These are the two little jokers that make Grouped Frequency tables so tricky.

1) THE CLASS BOUNDARIES are the precise values where you'd pass from one group into the next. For the above table the class boundaries would be at 40.5, 50.5, 60.5, etc. It's not difficult to work out what the class boundaries will be, just so long as you're clued up about it — they're nearly always "something.5" anyway, for obvious reasons.
2) THE MID-INTERVAL VALUES are pretty self-explanatory really and usually end up being "something.5" as well. Mind you a bit of care is needed to make sure you get the exact middle!

"Estimating" The Mean using Mid-Interval Values

Just like with ordinary frequency tables you have to add extra rows and find totals to be able to work anything out. Also notice you can only "estimate" the mean from grouped data tables — you can't find it exactly unless you know all the original values.

1) Add a 3rd row and enter MID-INTERVAL VALUES for each group.
2) Add a 4th row and multiply FREQUENCY × MID-INTERVAL VALUE for each group.

Weight (kg)	31 — 40	41 — 50	51 — 60	61 — 70	71 — 80	TOTALS
Frequency	8	16	18	12	6	60
Mid-Interval Value	35.5	45.5	55.5	65.5	75.5	—
Frequency × Mid-Interval Value	284	728	999	786	453	3250

1) ESTIMATING THE MEAN is then the usual thing of DIVIDING THE TOTALS:

$$\text{Mean} = \frac{\text{Overall Total (Final Row)}}{\text{Frequency Total (2nd Row)}} = \frac{3250}{60} = \underline{54.2}$$

2) THE MODE is still nice'n'easy: the modal group is 51 — 60kg (the one with the most entries).
3) THE MEDIAN can't be found exactly but you can at least say which group it's in. If all the data were put in order, the 30th/31st entries would be in the 51 — 60kg group.

The Acid Test:

LEARN all the details on this page, then turn over and write down everything you've learned. Good clean fun.

1) Estimate the mean for this table:
2) Also state the modal group and the approximate value of the median.

Length(cm)	15.5 —	16.5 —	17.5 —	18.5 — 19.5
Frequency	12	18	23	8

Cumulative Frequency Tables

Usually you'll get a half-finished table and they'll ask you to complete it as a cumulative frequency table. This means adding a third row and filling it in (as shown in the example below). Make sure you know these:

FOUR KEY POINTS

1) CUMULATIVE FREQUENCY just means ADDING IT UP AS YOU GO ALONG. So each entry in the table for cumulative frequency is just "THE TOTAL SO FAR".

2) You have to ADD A THIRD ROW to the table — this is just the RUNNING TOTAL of the 2nd row.

3) If you're plotting a graph, always plot points using the HIGHEST VALUE in each group (of row 1) with the value from row 3. (i.e. plot at the *class boundaries*) i.e. for the example below, plot 13 at 160.5, 33 at 170.5, etc.

4) CUMULATIVE FREQUENCY is always plotted up the side of a graph, not across.

Example

"Complete the table below for cumulative frequency:"

Height (cm)	141 – 150	151 – 160	161 – 170	171 – 180	181 – 190	191 – 200	201 – 210
Frequency	4	9	20	33	36	15	3

ANSWER: *Add in the third row* where each entry for row 3 (cumulative frequency) is just "THE TOTAL SO FAR" of the numbers for frequency (row 2).

Height (cm)	141 – 150	151 – 160	161 – 170	171 – 180	181 – 190	191 – 200	201 – 210
Frequency	4	9	20	33	36	15	3
Cumulative Frequency	4 (AT 150.5)	13 (AT 160.5)	33 (AT 170.5)	66 (AT 180.5)	102 (AT 190.5)	117 (AT 200.5)	120 (AT 210.5)

The graph is plotted from these pairs: (150.5, 4) (160.5, 13) (170.5, 33) (180.5, 66) etc. because the cumulative frequency has only reached those values (4, 13, 33 etc) by the TOP END of each group, not at the middle of each group, and *150.5* is the actual *CLASS BOUNDARY* between the first group and the next — a tricky detail.

The Acid Test:

LEARN the 4 Key Points, then turn over and write them down.

1) Complete the table shown here for cumulative frequency.

Weight (kg)	41 – 45	46 – 50	51 – 55	56 – 60	61 – 65	66 – 70	71 – 75
Frequency	2	7	17	25	19	8	2

The Cumulative Frequency Curve

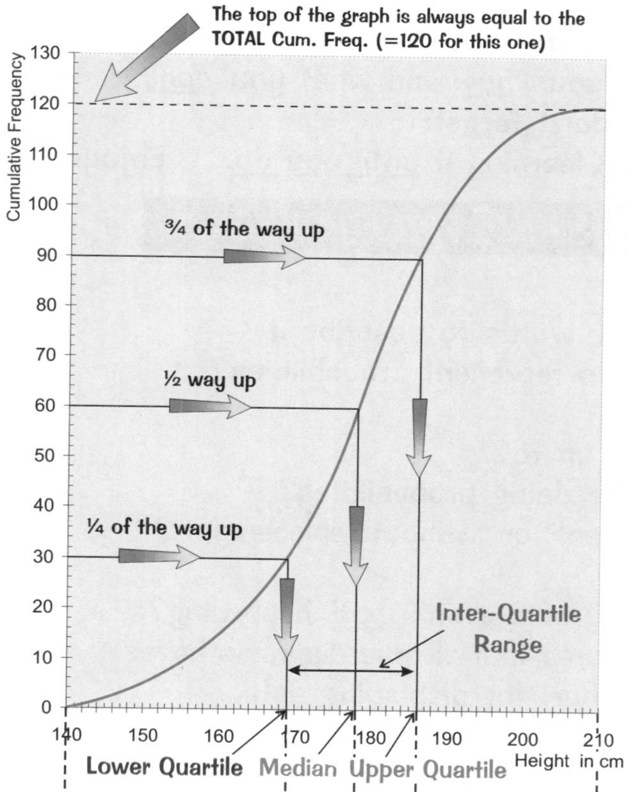

From the cumulative frequency curve you can get THREE VITAL STATISTICS:

1) **MEDIAN**
Exactly halfway UP, then across, then down and *read off the bottom scale*.
2) **LOWER AND UPPER QUARTILES**
Exactly ¼ and ¾ UP the side, then across, then down and *read off the bottom scale*.
3) **THE INTER-QUARTILE RANGE**
The distance *on the bottom scale* between the lower and upper quartiles.

So from the above cumulative frequency curve, we can easily get these results:

MEDIAN = 178cm
LOWER QUARTILE = 169cm
UPPER QUARTILE = 186cm
INTER-QUARTILE RANGE = 17cm (186-169)

A Box plot shows the Inter-Quartile Range as a Box

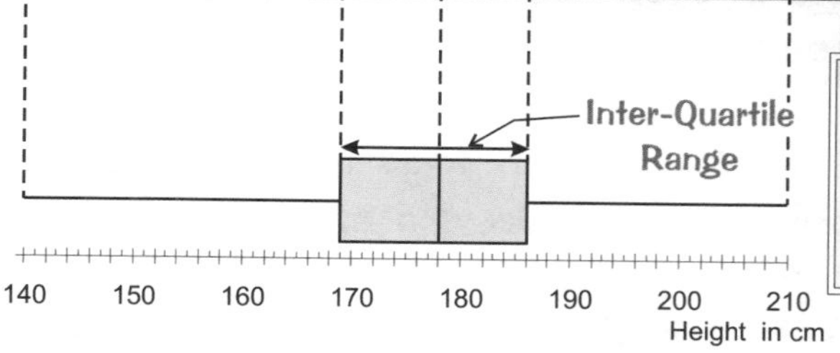

TO CREATE YOUR VERY OWN BOX PLOT:

1) *Draw the scale* along the bottom.
2) *Draw a box* the length of the *inter-quartile range*.
3) *Draw a line* down the box to show the *median*.
4) *Draw "whiskers"* up to the *maximum and minimum*.

(They're sometimes called "Box and Whisker diagrams".)

Interpreting The shape

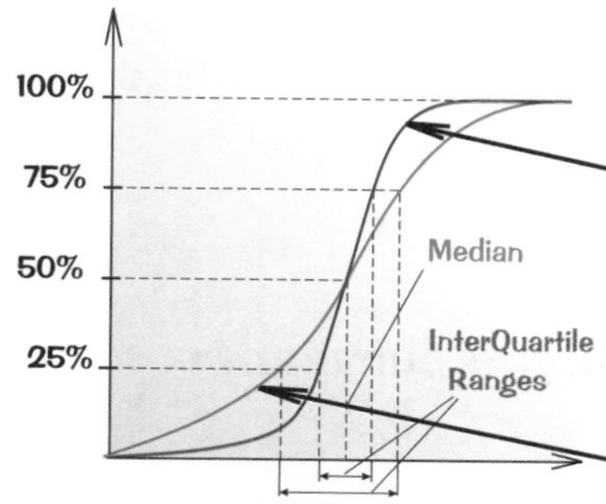

The shape of a CUMULATIVE FREQUENCY CURVE also tells you *how spread out* the data values are.

This 'tighter' distribution (which has a small interquartile range) represents very CONSISTENT results, which is usually good — e.g. *lifetimes of batteries or light bulbs* all very close together means a *good product*, compared to the other curve where the lifetimes show *wide variation*, i.e. poor quality product.

The Acid Test:

LEARN THIS PAGE, then cover it up and write down all the important details.

1) Using your completed frequency table from the previous page and draw the cumulative frequency graph and use it to find the three vital statistics.

Revision Test for Module One

Here's the really fun page. The inevitable list of straight-down-the-middle questions to test how much you know. Remember, these questions will sort out quicker than anything else can, exactly what you *know* and what you *don't*. And that's exactly what revision is all about, don't forget:

finding out what you DON'T know and then learning it until you do. Enjoy.

Keep learning these basic facts until you know them

1) How big or small can a probability be?
2) Draw a line to represent all probabilities with words to describe it.
3) Which three types of number can be used to represent probabilities?
4) How should $P(x) = ½$ be read?
5) What must the total probability always add up to?
6) Which calculator button is mighty useful for doing probabilities?
7) What is the full significance of "with replacement" or "without replacement"?
8) What are combined probabilities?
9) What can you say about the overall probability of 2 events *both* happening?
10) Draw a general tree diagram with all the features that all tree diagrams have.
11) Give the names of four different types of chart for displaying data.
12) Draw 2 examples of each type of chart.
13) When should the bars of a frequency chart touch and not touch?
14) What does correlation mean? Draw graphs showing the 3 different degrees.
15) What are the 3 steps for finding the angles in a pie chart?
16) Sketch the two different extremes of spread for histograms, and explain each one's significance.
17) Here's the results of a survey to find the number of soft toys owned by each member of a class of thirty primary school children. Draw a stem and leaf diagram of the results, using class widths of 5: 1, 9, 13, 20, 21, 29, 17, 13, 3, 32, 25, 27, 44, 31, 19, 7, 37, 24, 21, 43, 11, 23, 35, 27, 33, 17, 24, 26, 15, 22.
18) Give the definitions for mean, median, mode and range.
19) What are the eight key points for frequency tables?
20) How do you work out the mean and median from a frequency table?
21) How do you find the mode and range from a frequency table?
22) What's the difference between frequency tables and *grouped* frequency tables?
23) What are the 2 things that make grouped frequency tables so tricky?
24) How do you estimate the mean from a grouped frequency table?
25) What are the four key points for cumulative frequency?
26) Do you need to think about *class boundaries* when plotting a cumulative frequency curve from a table of values? Why?
27) Sketch a typical cumulative frequency graph.
28) What are the 3 vital statistics you can obtain from a C. F. graph?
29) Explain exactly how you obtain them, and illustrate on your graph.
30) What would you use a box plot for? Illustrate this on your graph.
31) How do you decide where halfway up the graph is?

Prime Numbers

1) Basically, PRIME Numbers don't divide by anything

And that's the best way to think of them.
So Prime Numbers are all the numbers that DON'T come up in Times Tables:

2 3 5 7 11 13 17 19 23 29 31 37 ...

As you can see, they're an awkward-looking bunch (that's because they don't divide by anything!). For example:

The only numbers that multiply to give 7 are	1×7
The only numbers that multiply to give 31 are	1×31

In fact the only way to get ANY PRIME NUMBER is $1 \times$ ITSELF

2) They All End in 1, 3, 7 or 9

1) 1 is NOT a prime number
2) The first four prime numbers are 2, 3, 5 and 7
3) 2 and 5 are the EXCEPTIONS because all the rest end in 1, 3, 7 or 9
4) But NOT ALL numbers ending in 1, 3, 7 or 9 are primes, as shown here: (Only the *circled ones* are *primes*)

(2)	(3)	(5)	(7)
(11)	(13)	(17)	(19)
21	(23)	27	(29)
(31)	33	(37)	39
(41)	(43)	(47)	49
51	(53)	57	(59)
(61)	63	(67)	69

3) HOW TO FIND PRIME NUMBERS — *a very simple method*

1) *Since all primes* (above 5) end in 1, 3, 7, or 9, then to find a prime number between say, 70 and 80, the only possibilities are: 71, 73, 77 and 79

2) Now, to find which of them ACTUALLY ARE primes you only need to divide each one by 3 and 7. If it doesn't divide exactly by either 3 or 7 then it's a prime.
(This simple rule using just 3 and 7 is true for checking primes *up to 120*)

So, to find the primes between 70 and 80, just try dividing 71, 73, 77 and 79 by 3 and 7:

$71 \div 3 = 23.667$, $71 \div 7 = 10.143$ so *71 IS* a prime number
(*because it ends in 1, 3, 7 or 9 and it doesn't divide by 3 or 7*)

$73 \div 3 = 24.333$, $73 \div 7 = 10.429$ so *73 IS* a prime number

$79 \div 3 = 26.333$ $79 \div 7 = 11.286$ so *79 IS* a prime number

$77 \div 3 = 25.667$ BUT: $77 \div 7 = 11$ — 11 is a whole number (*or 'integer'*),
so 77 is NOT a prime, because it will *divide by 7* ($7 \times 11 = 77$)

The Acid Test: LEARN the main points in ALL 3 SECTIONS above.

Now cover the page and write down everything you've just learned.
1) Write down the first 15 prime numbers (*without* looking them up).
2) Using the above method, find all the prime numbers between 90 and 110.

Multiples, Factors and Prime Factors

Multiples

The MULTIPLES of a number are simply its TIMES TABLE:

E.g. the multiples of 13 are 13 26 39 52 65 78 91 104 ...

Factors

The FACTORS of a number are all the numbers that DIVIDE INTO IT. There's a special way to find them:

Example 1: *"Find ALL the factors of 24".*

Start off with 1× the number itself, then try 2×, then 3× and so on, listing the pairs in rows like this. Try each one in turn and put a dash if it doesn't divide exactly. Eventually, when you get a number *repeated*, you *stop*.

Increasing by 1 each time

1 × 24
2 × 12
3 × 8
4 × 6
5 × –
6 × 4

So the FACTORS OF 24 are 1,2,3,4,6,8,12,24

This method guarantees you find them ALL — but *don't forget 1 and 24!*

Factors Example 2: *"Find the factors of 64".*

1 × 64
2 × 32
3 × –
4 × 16
5 × –
6 × –
7 × –
8 × 8

Check each one in turn, to see if it divides or not. Use your calculator when you can, if you're not totally confident.

The 8 has *repeated* so *stop here*.

So the FACTORS of 64 are 1,2,4,8,16,32,64

Finding Prime Factors — The Factor Tree

Any number can be broken down into a string of PRIME NUMBERS (see P.15) all multiplied together — this is called "Expressing it as a product of prime factors", and to be honest it's pretty tedious — but it's in the Exam, and it's not difficult so long as you know what it is.

The mildly entertaining "Factor Tree" method is best, where you start at the top and split your number off into factors as shown. Each time you get a prime, you ring it and you finally end up with all the prime factors, which you can then arrange in order.

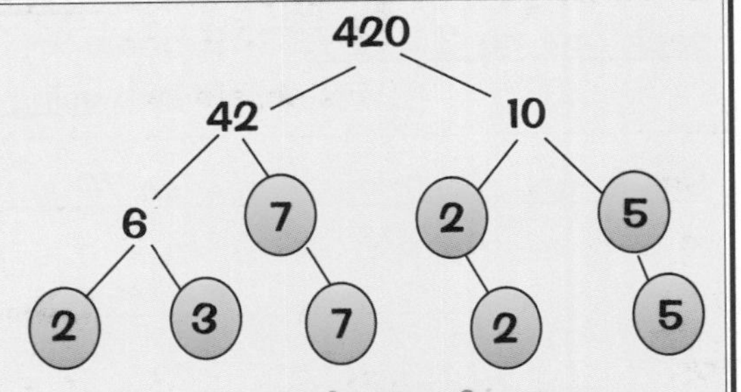

So, "As a *product of prime factors*", 420 = 2×2×3×5×7

The Acid Test:

Then try these without the notes:

1) List the first 10 multiples of 7, and the first 10 multiples of 9.
2) List all the factors of 36 and all the factors of 84.
3) Express as a product of prime factors: a) 990 b) 160.

LCM and HCF

Two big fancy names but don't be put off — they're both *real easy*.

LCM — "Lowest Common Multiple"

"*Lowest Common Multiple*" — sure, it sounds kind of complicated but *all it means is this*:

The *SMALLEST* number that will *DIVIDE BY ALL* the numbers in question.

Method

1) *LIST* the *MULTIPLES* of *ALL* the numbers.
2) Find the *SMALLEST* one that's in *ALL the lists*.
3) Easy peasy innit.

Example *Find the lowest common multiple (LCM) of 6 and 7*

Answer Multiples of 6 are: 6, 12, 18, 24, 30, 36, (42), 48, 54, 60, 66, ...
Multiples of 7 are: 7, 14, 21, 28, 35, (42), 49, 56, 63, 70, 77, ...

So the *lowest common multiple* (LCM) of 6 and 7 is *42*.
Told you it was easy.

HCF — "Highest Common Factor"

"*Highest Common Factor*" — all it means is *this*:

The *BIGGEST* number that will *DIVIDE INTO ALL* the numbers in question.

Method

1) *LIST* the *FACTORS* of *all* the numbers.
2) Find the *BIGGEST* one that's in *ALL the lists*.
3) Easy peasy innit.

Example *Find the highest common factor (HCF) of 36, 54, and 72*

Answer Factors of 36 are: 1, 2, 3, 4, 6, 9, 12, (18), 36
Factors of 54 are: 1, 2, 3, 6, 9, (18), 27, 54
Factors of 72 are: 1, 2, 3, 4, 6, 8, 9, 12, (18), 24, 36, 72

So the *highest common factor* (HCF) of 36, 54 and 72 is *18*.
Told you it was easy.

Just *take care* listing the factors — make sure you use the *proper method* (as shown on the previous page) or you'll miss one and blow the whole thing out of the water.

The Acid Test:

LEARN what LCM and HCF are, AND HOW TO FIND THEM. Turn over and write it all down.

1) List the first 10 multiples of 8, and the first 10 multiples of 9. What's their LCM?
2) List all the factors of 56 and all the factors of 104. What's their HCF?
3) What's the Lowest Common Multiple of 7 and 9?
4) What's the Highest Common Factor of 36 and 84?

Powers (or "Indices")

Powers are a very useful shorthand:

$2\times2\times2\times2\times2\times2\times2 = 2^7$ ("two to the power 7")
$7\times7 = 7^2$ ("7 squared")
$6\times6\times6\times6\times6 = 6^5$ (" Six to the power 5")
$4\times4\times4 = 4^3$ ("four cubed")

That bit is easy to remember. Unfortunately, there are SEVEN SPECIAL RULES for Powers that are not quite so easy, but *you do need to know them for the Exam*:

Also in module 5:

The Seven Rules

1) When MULTIPLYING, you ADD the powers.

e.g. $3^4 \times 3^6 = 3^{6+4} = 3^{10}$ $\quad$ $8^3 \times 8^5 = 8^{3+5} = 8^8$

2) When DIVIDING, you SUBTRACT the powers.

e.g. $5^4 \div 5^2 = 5^{4-2} = 5^2$ $\quad$ $12^8/12^3 = 12^{8-3} = 12^5$

3) When RAISING one power to another, you MULTIPLY the powers.

e.g. $(3^2)^4 = 3^{2\times4} = 3^8$, $\quad$ $(5^4)^6 = 5^{24}$

4) $X^1 = X$, ANYTHING TO THE POWER 1 is just ITSELF.

e.g. $3^1 = 3$, $\quad$ $6 \times 6^3 = 6^4$, $\quad$ $4^3 \div 4^2 = 4^{3-2} = 4^1 = 4$

5) $X^0 = 1$, ANYTHING TO THE POWER 0 is just 1.

e.g. $5^0 = 1$ $\quad$ $67^0 = 1$ $\quad$ $3^4/3^4 = 3^{4-4} = 3^0 = 1$

6) $1^x = 1$, 1 TO ANY POWER is still just 1.

e.g. $1^{23} = 1$ $\quad$ $1^{89} = 1$ $\quad$ $1^2 = 1$ $\quad$ $1^{1012} = 1$

7) FRACTIONAL POWERS mean one thing: ROOTS.

The Power ½ means *Square Root*, e.g. $25^{\frac{1}{2}} = \sqrt{25} = 5$

The Power ⅓ means *Cube Root*, e.g. $64^{\frac{1}{3}} = \sqrt[3]{64} = 4$

The Acid Test:

LEARN the Seven Rules for Powers. Then turn over and write it all down. Keep trying until you can do it!

Then cover the page and apply the rules to SIMPLIFY these:

1) a) $3^2 \times 3^6$ b) $4^3 \div 4^2$ c) $(8^3)^4$ d) $(3^2 \times 3^3 \times 1^6)/3^5$ e) $7^3 \times 7 \times 7^2$

2) a) $5^2 \times 5^7 \times 5^3$ b) $1^3 \times 5^0 \times 6^2$ c) $(4^3 \times 4 \times 4^2) \div (2^3 \times 2^4)$

3) If $6\times6\times6 = 216$, what is the value of $216^{\frac{1}{3}}$?

Square & Cube Numbers and Square Roots

Square Numbers

They're called SQUARE NUMBERS because they're like the areas of this pattern of squares:

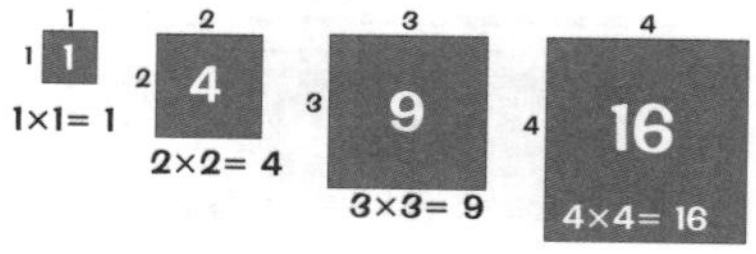

(1×1)	(2×2)	(3×3)	(4×4)	(5×5)	(6×6)	(7×7)	(8×8)	(9×9)	(10×10)	(11×11)	(12×12)	(13×13)	(14×14)	(15×15)
1	4	9	16	25	36	49	64	81	100	121	144	169	196	225...

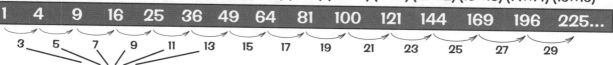

Differences: 3 5 7 9 11 13 15 17 19 21 23 25 27 29

Note that the DIFFERENCES between the square numbers are all the ODD numbers.

Cube Numbers

They're called CUBE NUMBERS because they're like the volumes of this pattern of cubes.

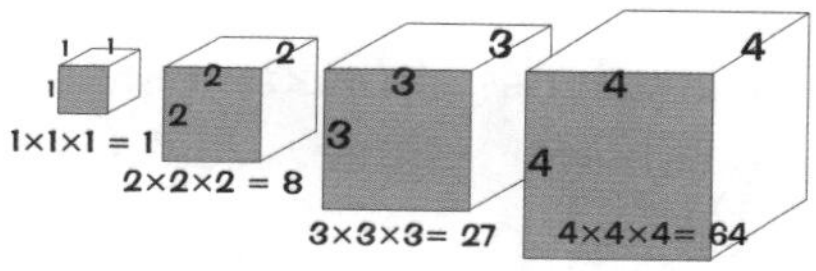

(1x1x1)	(2x2x2)	(3x3x3)	(4x4x4)	(5x5x5)	(6x6x6)	(7x7x7)	(8x8x8)	(9x9x9)	(10x10x10)...
1	8	27	64	125	216	343	512	729	1000...

Admit it, you never knew maths could be this exciting did you!

Square Roots

"Squared" means "times by itself" : $P^2 = P \times P$
— SQUARE ROOT is the reverse process.

The best way to think of it is this:

"Square Root" means
"What Number Times by Itself gives..."

Example: *"Find the square root of 49"* (i.e. " Find $\sqrt{49}$ " or "Find $49^{1/2}$ ")

To do this you should say it as: *"What number TIMES BY ITSELF gives... 49"*

Now, if you learn the number sequences above, then of course you'll know instantly that the answer is 7.

On your calculator, *it's easy to find any positive square root* using the SQUARE ROOT BUTTON: Press [√] [49] [=] = 7 (See P.39)

Square Roots can be Positive or Negative

If you multiply a negative number by itself, you get a positive one (see P.22):

$(-2)^2 = (-2) \times (-2) = 4$ But $2^2 = 4$ as well. (What's going on...)

It's actually quite simple: $\sqrt{4} = +2$ or -2

... and that goes for all square roots —
whenever you get a positive square root, you also get a negative one.

Also in module 5:

Square Roots and Cube Roots

Also in module 5:

Estimating Square Roots

Looks horrible — but it's OK if you know your square numbers.

1) Find the TWO SQUARE NUMBERS EITHER SIDE of the number in question.
2) Find the SQUARE ROOTS and pick a SENSIBLE NUMBER IN BETWEEN.

EXAMPLE: "Estimate $\sqrt{85}$ without using a calculator."

① The square numbers either side of 85 are 81 and 100.

② The square roots are 9 and 10, so $\sqrt{85}$ must be between 9 and 10. But 85 is much nearer 81 than 100, so $\sqrt{85}$ must be much nearer 9 than 10. So pick 9.1, 9.2 or 9.3.
(The answer's actually 9.2195... if you're interested.)

Keeping the Square Root Sign

The square root of any number that isn't a square number will give you a really long decimal answer. Most of the time you can round this off sensibly.

Sometimes it makes sense not to work out the square root, especially if you haven't got a calculator to use. Just leave your answer with a square root sign in it.

Example: "A square has area 40cm^2. How long is each side of the square?"

Answer: The length of the sides is $\sqrt{40}$. If you have a calculator, then you can work out $\sqrt{40}$ = 6.3245553 ... If you haven't got a calculator, then just write $\sqrt{40}$.

Cube Roots

"Cubed" means "times by itself three times" : $T^3 = T \times T \times T$
— CUBE ROOT is the reverse process.

"Cube Root" means "What Number Times by Itself THREE TIMES gives..."

Well, strictly there are only two × signs, but you know what I mean.

Example: *"Find the cube root of 64"* (i.e "Find $\sqrt[3]{64}$" or " Find $64^{\frac{1}{3}}$")

You should say: *"What number TIMES BY ITSELF THREE TIMES gives... 64"*
From your in-depth revision of P.19 you will of course know the answer is 4.

OR on your calculator just use the CUBE ROOT BUTTON:

Press [$\sqrt[3]{\ }$] [27] [=] = 3 (See P.39)

And Don't Forget:

"SOMETHING TO THE POWER ½" is just a different way of asking for a SQUARE ROOT
e.g. $81^{\frac{1}{2}}$ is the same as $\sqrt{81}$ which is just 9.
"SOMETHING TO THE POWER 1/3" is just a different way of asking for a CUBE ROOT
e.g. $27^{\frac{1}{3}}$ is the same as $\sqrt[3]{27}$ which is just 3.

The Acid Test:

LEARN the best method for finding roots and what fractional powers mean. Then turn the page and write it all down.

1) Use your calculator to find a) $56^{\frac{1}{2}}$ b) $450^{\frac{1}{3}}$ c) $\sqrt{40}$ d) $\sqrt[3]{8000}$.
For a) and c), what are the other values that your calculator didn't give?
2) a) If $g^2 = 36$, find g. b) If $b^3 = 64$, find b. c) If $4 \times r^2 = 36$, find r.

Multiplying and Dividing

1) TO MULTIPLY BY 10, 100, 1000:

Move the Decimal Point so many places BIGGER and ADD ZEROS if necessary.

Examples:

341 × 1000 = 341000

2.3542 × 10,000 = 23542

You always *move* the *DECIMAL POINT* this much:
1 place for 10, 2 places for 100, 3 places for 1000, 4 for 10,000 etc.

2) TO MULTIPLY BY NUMBERS LIKE 20, 300, 8000 ETC.

Multiply by 2 or 3 or 8 etc. FIRST, then move the Decimal Point so many places BIGGER ( ) according to how many noughts there are.

Example:

To find 234 × 200, *first multiply by 2* 234 × 2 = 468,
then *move the DP 2 places* = 46800

3) TO DIVIDE BY 10, 100, OR 1000:

Move the Decimal Point so many places SMALLER and REMOVE ZEROS after the decimal point.

Examples:

341 ÷ 1000 = 0.341

23542 ÷ 10,000 = 2.3542

You always *move* the *DECIMAL POINT* this much:
1 place for 10, 2 places for 100, 3 places for 1000, 4 for 10,000 etc.

4) DIVIDING BY 40, 300, 7000 ETC.

DIVIDE BY 4 or 3 or 7 etc. FIRST and then move the Decimal Point so many places SMALLER (i.e. to the left).

Example:

To find 960 ÷ 300, *first divide by 3* 960 ÷ 3 = 320,
then *move the DP 2 places smaller* = 3.2

Negative Numbers and Reciprocals

Rule

Only to be used when:

+	+	makes	+
+	–	makes	–
–	+	makes	–
–	–	makes	+

1) Multiplying or dividing

e.g. -2 x 3 = –6, -8 ÷ -2 = +4 -4p x -2 = +8p

2) Two signs appear next to each other

e.g. 5 – -4 = 5+4 = 9 4 + -6 – -7 = 4 – 6 + 7 = 5

Reciprocals

Usually when you multiply a number it gets bigger. However, if you multiply by a number less than 1, the other number gets smaller.
To see why this happens, we have to learn a bit about fractions.

The RECIPROCAL of a fraction is just what you get when you turn it upside down.

The reciprocal of $\frac{2}{3}$ is $\frac{3}{2}$, and the reciprocal of $\frac{5}{8}$ is $\frac{8}{5}$.

A UNIT FRACTION is just one with a one on the top (unit means one).

So $\frac{1}{2}$, $\frac{1}{3}$, $\frac{1}{237}$ are all unit fractions.

The reciprocal of a unit fraction is just the number on the bottom.

For example, the reciprocal of $\frac{1}{4}$ is 4.

Multiplying and Dividing by Fractions

The rules are
1) Multiplying by a fraction is the same as dividing by the reciprocal.
2) Dividing by a fraction is the same as multiplying by the reciprocal.

Example:

Work out $35 \times \frac{1}{5}$ — The reciprocal of $\frac{1}{5}$ is 5 so $35 \times \frac{1}{5} = 35 \div 5 = 7$

Work out $4 \div \frac{1}{3}$ — The reciprocal of $\frac{1}{3}$ is 3 so $4 \div \frac{1}{3} = 4 \times 3 = 12$

The Acid Test:

1) Work out: a) -4×-3 b) $-4 + -5 + 3$ c) $120 \div -40$
2) Write down the reciprocals of a) $\frac{1}{7}$ b) $\frac{4}{5}$
3) Work out: a) $60 \div \frac{1}{2}$ b) $24 \times \frac{1}{3}$ c) $10 \div \frac{1}{5}$

Fractions, Decimals and Percentages

The one word that could describe all these three is PROPORTION. Fractions, decimals and percentages are simply three different ways of expressing a proportion of something — and it's pretty important you should see them as closely related and completely interchangeable with each other. This table shows the really common conversions which you should know straight off without having to work them out:

Fraction	Decimal	Percentage
1/2	0.5	50%
1/4	0.25	25%
3/4	0.75	75%
1/3	0.333333	33%
2/3	0.666667	67%
1/10	0.1	10%
2/10	0.2	20%
X/10	0.X	X0%
1/5	0.2	20%
2/5	0.4	40%

⅓ and ⅔ have what're known as 'recurring' decimals — the same pattern of numbers carries on repeating itself forever. (Except here, the pattern's just a single 3 or a single 6. You could have, for instance: 0.143143143...) The ⅔ decimal ends in a 7 because it's been rounded up.

The more of those conversions you learn, the better — but for those that you don't know, you must also learn how to convert between the three types. These are the methods:

Fraction → Divide (use your calculator if you can) → Decimal → × by 100 → Percentage

e.g. ½ is 1÷2 = 0.5 e.g. 0.5 × 100 = 50%

Fraction ← The tricky one ← Decimal ← ÷ by 100 ← Percentage

Converting decimals to fractions is only possible for exact decimals that haven't been rounded off.

It's simple enough, but it's best illustrated by examples so look now at P.24 and work out what the simple rule is. You should then be able to fill in the rest of this table:

Fraction	Decimal	Percentage
1/5		
	0.35	
		45%
	0.12	
1/8		
	0.77	

The Acid Test:

LEARN the whole of the top table and the 4 conversion processes for FDP.

Now cover the page and write out the top FDP table from memory, and then the four conversion rules. Then fill in all the spaces in the 2nd table shown above.

Fractions Without the Calculator

Doing fractions *by hand* is always a pest... so you'd better learn this little lot before your exam!

1) Converting Fractions to Decimals — Just DIVIDE

Just remember that " / " means "÷", so ¼ means 1 ÷ 4 = 0.25

The *denominator* (bottom number) of a fraction, tells you if it'll be a *recurring* or *terminating decimal* when you convert it.

only *prime* factors: 2 & 5

FRACTION	$\frac{1}{5}$	$\frac{1}{125}$	$\frac{1}{2}$	$\frac{1}{20}$
EQUIVALENT DECIMAL	0.2	0.008	0.5	0.05

For prime factors, see P. 15

also *other* prime factors

$\frac{1}{7}$	$\frac{1}{35}$	$\frac{1}{3}$	$\frac{1}{6}$
0.142857	0.0285714	0.3333	0.16666

Fractions where the denominator has *prime factors* of *only 2 or 5* will give *terminating decimals*. All *other fractions* will give *recurring decimals*.

2) Converting Decimals to Fractions

— it's a simple rule, so work it out yourself!:

0.6 = $\frac{6}{10}$, 0.3 = $\frac{3}{10}$, 0.7 = 7/10, 0.X = X/10, etc.

0.12 = $\frac{12}{100}$, 0.78 = $\frac{78}{100}$, 0.45 = 45/100, 0.05 = 5/100, etc.

These can then be *cancelled down*.

0.345 = $\frac{345}{1000}$, 0.908 = 908/1000, 0.024 = 24/1000, 0.XYZ = XYZ/1000, etc.

And remember — all *recurring* decimals are just (exact) fractions in disguise.

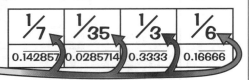

1) Multiplying — easy

Multiply top and bottom separately:

$$\frac{3}{5}\times\frac{4}{7}=\frac{3\times4}{5\times7}=\frac{12}{35}$$

2) Dividing — quite easy

Turn the 2nd fraction *UPSIDE DOWN* and then multiply:

$$\frac{3}{4}\div\frac{1}{3}=\frac{3}{4}\times\frac{3}{1}=\frac{3\times3}{4\times1}=\frac{9}{4}$$

3) Adding, subtracting — fraught

Add or subtract *TOP LINES ONLY* but *only if the bottom numbers are the same.* (If they're not the same it gets very tricky — see opposite.)

$$\frac{3}{6}+\frac{1}{6}=\frac{3}{6}$$

$$\frac{5}{7}-\frac{3}{7}=\frac{2}{7}$$

4) Cancelling down — easy

Divide top and bottom by the same number, till they won't go any further:

$$\frac{18}{24}\overset{\div3}{=}\frac{6}{8}\overset{\div2}{=}\frac{3}{4}$$

5) Finding a fraction of something — just multiply.

Multiply the 'something' by the *TOP* of the fraction, then *divide* it by the *BOTTOM*:

$$\frac{9}{20}\text{ of } £360 = \{(9)\times360\}\div(20) = \frac{£3240}{20} = £162$$

$$\text{or } \frac{9}{20}\text{ of } £360 = \{\frac{9}{1}\times £360\}\times\frac{1}{20} = £162$$

More Fractions

6) Equalising the Denominator — why oh why...

You need this whether you're using your *calculator or not*. It comes in handy with ordering fractions by size, and you need it for addition and subtraction by hand. To make the bottom number the same, you need to find a common multiple of all the denominators:

Example: Put these fractions in ascending order of size: $\frac{8}{3}$, $\frac{6}{4}$, $\frac{12}{5}$

⟹ Lowest Common Multiple = 3 × 4 × 5 = 60 ⟹ $\frac{8}{3} = \frac{8}{3} \times \frac{20}{20} = \frac{160}{60}$

See P.16 so put all the fractions over 60... $\frac{6}{4} = \frac{6}{4} \times \frac{15}{15} = \frac{90}{60}$ ⟹ $\frac{90}{60}$, $\frac{144}{60}$, $\frac{160}{60}$

(remember that anything divided by itself = 1) $\frac{12}{5} = \frac{12}{5} \times \frac{12}{12} = \frac{144}{60}$ *OR:* $\frac{6}{4}$, $\frac{12}{5}$, $\frac{8}{3}$

When you can though, use your calculator to do all fractions in your exams. It makes sense...

The Fraction Button: [a b/c]

Use this as much as possible in the Exam.
It's very easy, so make sure you know how to use it — or you'll lose a lot of marks:

1) TO ENTER A NORMAL FRACTION like ¼ Just press: [1] [a b/c] [4]

2) TO ENTER A MIXED FRACTION like 1 ⅗ Just press: [1] [a b/c] [3] [a b/c] [5]

3) TO DO A REGULAR CALCULATION such as ⅕ × ¾
Just press: [1] [a b/c] [5] [X] [3] [a b/c] [4] [=]

4) TO REDUCE A FRACTION TO ITS LOWEST TERMS
Just enter it and then press [=]
e.g. $\frac{9}{12}$, [9] [a b/c] [12] [=] 3⌟4 = ¾

5) TO CONVERT BETWEEN MIXED AND TOP HEAVY FRACTIONS

Just press [SHIFT] [a b/c] e.g. to give $2\frac{3}{8}$ as a top heavy fraction:
Press: [2] [a b/c] [3] [a b/c] [8] [=] to enter the fraction, then [SHIFT] [a b/c] to convert it to $\frac{19}{8}$.

The Acid Test:

LEARN the 2 Rules for converting Fractions ↔ Decimals, the 4 Manual Methods and the 5 features of the Fraction Button.

Then cover up these two pages and write down what you've learned.

1) Do these *WITH YOUR CALCULATOR*:

a) 1/2 x 3/4 b) 3/5 ÷ 2/9 c) 1/3 + 2/5 d) Find x: $2\frac{3}{5} = \frac{x}{5}$ e) Find y: $\frac{14}{98} = \frac{y}{7}$
f) Convert 3/8 into a decimal. g) Convert 0.035 into a fraction, and cancel it down.

2) Do these *BY HAND*:

a) 2/3 x 4/5 b) 4/5 ÷ 3/10 c) 5/6 – 2/6 d) Express 36/84 in its simplest form.
e) Work out 12/19 × 133. f) Work out 12/19 × 134. Express your answer as a fraction.
(Pssssst... what that means is that rather than a decimal of e.g. 1.25, you'd give the answer as 1¼. Make sure you can do that — 'coz they could ask you it in the Exam.)

Percentages

Contrary to popular belief there are *three distinct types* of percentage question. Obviously then, it's going to be pretty *essential* that you can:

1) Distinguish between the three types
2) Remember the METHOD for each of them

Type 1

— THESE ARE IDENTIFIED BY THE "%" SYMBOL IN THE QUESTION

This is the easiest type — they're always of the form:

FIND "something" % OF "something-else"

For example: Find 15% *of* £25

Method

1) WRITE: 15% OF £25 (↓ ↓ ↓)
2) TRANSLATE: $\frac{15}{100} \times 25 = £3.75$
3) CHECK THAT IT'S A SENSIBLE ANSWER.

Remember:

1) "OF" means "×"
2) "PER CENT" means "OUT OF 100", so 15% *means* "15 out of 100", i.e. $\frac{15}{100}$

Also in module 5:

Type 2

— THESE ARE IDENTIFIED BY THE WORD "PERCENTAGE" IN THE QUESTION

These are always of the form:

EXPRESS "one thing" AS A PERCENTAGE OF "another"

For example: Express 35p *as a percentage* of £2.80

Method — FDP

FDP : Fraction – Decimal – Percentage

(See P.23)

$\frac{35}{280} \xrightarrow{35 \div 280} 0.125 \xrightarrow{\times 100} 12.5\%$

Make a fraction using the two numbers — always with the smallest on top

Divide them to get a decimal

Then multiply by 100 to get a percentage

Percentages

Type 3 — THESE ARE IDENTIFIED BY THEM *NOT* GIVING YOU THE *"ORIGINAL VALUE"*

These are the type most people get wrong — but only because they don't recognise them as a type 3 and don't apply this simple method:

Example:

A house increases in value by 20% to £72,000. Find its value *before* the rise.

Method

	£72,000	=	120%
÷ 120	£600	=	1%
× 100	£60,000	=	100%

So the original price was **£60,000**

An *increase* of 20% means that £72,000 represents *120% of the original* value.
If it was a *DROP* of 20%, then we would put "*£72,000 = 80%*" instead, and then divide by *80* on the LHS, instead of 120.

Always set them out exactly like this example. The trickiest bit is deciding the top % figure on the RHS — the 2nd and 3rd rows are *always* 1% and 100%

Also in module 5:

Percentage Change (*An important example of type 2*)

It's quite common to give a *change in value* as a *percentage*.
This is the formula for doing so — *LEARN IT, AND USE IT:*

$$\text{PERCENTAGE "CHANGE"} = \frac{\text{"CHANGE"}}{\text{ORIGINAL}} \times 100$$

By "change", we could mean all sorts of things such as: "Profit", "loss", "appreciation", "depreciation", "increase", "decrease", "error", "discount", etc. For example, *percentage "profit"* $= \frac{\text{"profit"}}{\text{original}} \times 100$.

Don't forget the monster importance of using the *ORIGINAL VALUE* in this formula.

The Acid Test:

LEARN The 3 Types, how you identify them, and the Method for each. Also LEARN the Formula for Percentage Change.

Now *turn over and write down all the details* you've just learned.

Identify the following questions as Type 1, 2, or 3, and apply the method for each.
Practise until you can do them without the notes:

1) A trader buys watches for £5 and sells them for £7. Find his profit in £ and then express it as a percentage.
2) Find the total cost of a plumber's bill given as: "£36 + 17.5% VAT".
3) A car depreciates by 30% to £14,350. What was it worth before?

Compound Growth and Decay

This can also be called "Exponential" Growth or Decay. But you don't want to know that.

You want to know this:

The Formula

This topic is simple if you LEARN THIS FORMULA. If you don't, it's pretty well impossible:

$$N = N_0(1 + {}^{r}\!/_{100})^n$$

- N — Existing amount at this time
- N_0 — Initial amount
- r — Percentage change per day/hour/year
- n — Number of days/hrs/yrs

Percentage Increase and Decrease

The (1+ r/100) bit might look a bit confusing in the formula but in practice it's really easy:

E.g 5% increase will be 1.05 5% decrease will be 0.95 (= 1 – 0.05)

26% increase will be 1.26 26% decrease will be 0.74 (= 1 – 0.26)

3 Examples to show you how EASY it is:

1) *"A man invests £1000 in a savings account which pays 8% per annum. How much will there be after 6 years?"*

ANSWER: Usual formula (as above): Amount $= 1000\times(1.08)^6 =$ £1586.87

(1000 = Initial amount, 1.08 = 8% increase, 6 = 6 years)

2) *"The activity of a radio-isotope falls by 12% every hour. If the initial activity is 800 counts per minute, what will it be after 7 hours?"*

ANSWER: Same old formula:

Activity = Initial value$(1 - 12/100)^n$

Activity $= 800(1 - 0.12)^7 = 800\times(0.88)^7 =$ 327 cpm

3) *"In a sample of bacteria, there are initially 500 cells and they increase in number by 15% each day. Find the formula relating the number of cells, n, and the number of days, d."*

ANSWER: Well stone me, it's the same old easy-peasy compound increase formula again:

$n = n_0(1+0.15)^d$ or finished off: $n = 500\times(1.15)^d$

The Acid Test:

LEARN THE FORMULA. Also learn the 3 Examples. Then turn over and write it all down.

1) The population of a colony of stick insects increases by 4% per week. Initially there are 30. How many will there be after 12 weeks?
2) The speed of a tennis ball rolled along a smooth floor falls by 16% every second. If the initial speed was 5m/s find the speed after 20 seconds.

Ratios

The whole grisly subject of RATIOS gets a whole lot easier when you do this:

Treat RATIOS like FRACTIONS

So for the RATIO 3:4, you'd treat it as the FRACTION 3/4, which is 0.75 as a DECIMAL.

What the fraction form of the ratio actually means

Suppose in a class there's girls and boys in the ratio 3 : 4.
This means there's 3/4 as many girls as boys.
So if there were 20 boys, there would be 3/4 × 20 = 15 girls.
You've got to be careful — it doesn't mean 3/4 of the people in the class are girls.

Reducing Ratios to their simplest form

You reduce ratios just like you'd reduce fractions to their simplest form.

For the ratio 15 : 18, both numbers have a factor of 3, so divide them by 3 —
That gives 5 : 6. We can't reduce this any further. So the simplest form of 15 : 18 is 5 : 6.

Treat them just like fractions — use your calculator if you can

Now this is really sneaky. If you stick in a fraction using the $a^b/_c$ button, your calculator automatically cancels it down when you press =.

So for the ratio 8 : 12, just press 8 $a^b/_c$ 12 = , and you'll get the reduced fraction 2/3.
Now you just change it back to ratio form i.e. 2 : 3. Ace.

The More Awkward Cases:

1) The $a^b/_c$ button will only accept whole numbers

So IF THE RATIO IS AWKWARD (like "2.4 : 3.6" or "1¼ : 3½") then you must:
MULTIPLY BOTH SIDES by the SAME NUMBER until they are both WHOLE NUMBERS
and then you can use the $a^b/_c$ button as before to simplify them down.
e.g. with "1¼ : 3½", × both sides by 4 gives "5 : 14" (Try $a^b/_c$, but it won't cancel further)

2) If the ratio is MIXED UNITS

then you must CONVERT BOTH SIDES into the *SMALLER UNITS* using the relevant CONVERSION FACTOR (see P.31), and then carry on as normal.
e.g. "24mm : 7.2cm" (× 7.2cm by 10) ⇒ 24mm : 72mm = 1 : 3 (using $a^b/_c$)

3) To reduce a ratio to the form 1 : n

(*n can be any number at all*)

Simply DIVIDE BOTH SIDES BY THE *SMALLEST SIDE*.
e.g. take "3 : 56" — dividing both sides by 3 gives: 1 : 18.7 (56÷3) (i.e. 1 : n)
The 1 : n form is often the *most useful*, since it shows the ratio very clearly.

Ratios

Using The Formula Triangle in Ratio Questions

"Mortar is made from sand and cement in the ratio 7:2.
If 9 buckets of sand are used, how much cement is needed?"

This is a fairly common type of Exam question and it's pretty tricky for most people — but once you start using the formula triangle method, it's all a bit of a breeze really.

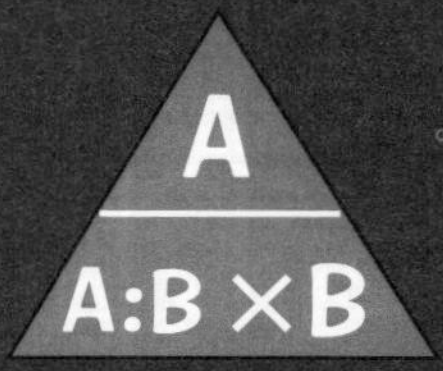

This is the basic FORMULA TRIANGLE for RATIOS, but NOTE:

1) THE RATIO MUST BE THE RIGHT WAY ROUND, with the FIRST NUMBER IN THE RATIO relating to the item ON TOP in the triangle.

2) You'll always need to CONVERT THE RATIO into its EQUIVALENT FRACTION or Decimal to work out the answer.

The formula triangle for the mortar question is shown below and the trick is to replace the RATIO 7:2 by its EQUIVALENT FRACTION: 7/2, or 3.5 as a decimal (7÷2)

So, *covering up cement in the triangle*, gives us "cement = sand / (7:2)"
i.e. "9 / 3.5" = 9 ÷ 3.5 = 2.57 or about *2½ buckets of cement*.

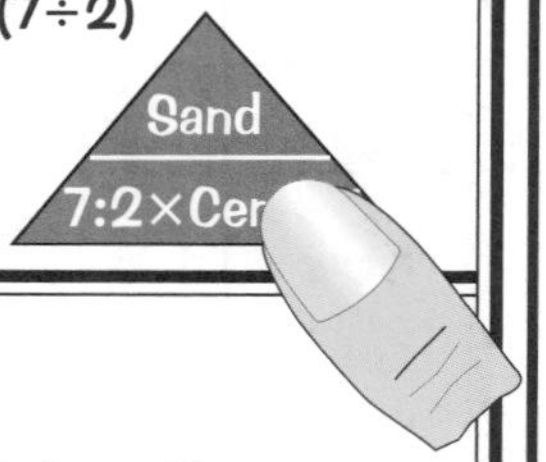

Proportional Division

In a *proportional division question* a *TOTAL AMOUNT* is to be *split in a certain ratio*.

For example: *"£9100 is to be split in the ratio 2:4:7. Find the 3 amounts"*.

The key word here is PARTS. — concentrate on "parts" and it all becomes quite painless:

Method

1) ADD UP THE PARTS:
The ratio 2:4:7 means there will be a total of 13 *parts* i.e. 2+4+7 = 13 PARTS

2) FIND THE AMOUNT FOR ONE *"PART"*:
Just *divide* the *total amount* by the number of *parts:* £9100 ÷ 13 = £700 (= 1 PART)

3) HENCE FIND THE THREE AMOUNTS:
2 parts = 2×700 = £1400, 4 parts = 4×700 = £2800, 7 parts = £4900

The Acid Test:

LEARN the 6 RULES for SIMPLIFYING, the FORMULA TRIANGLE for Ratios (plus 2 points), and the 3 Steps for PROPORTIONAL DIVISION.

Now *turn over* and *write down what you've learned*. Try again *until you can do it*.

1) Simplify: a) 25:35 b) 3.4 : 5.1 c) 2¼ : 3¾
2) Porridge and ice-cream are mixed in the ratio 7:4 . How much porridge should go with 10 bowls of ice-cream?
3) Divide £8400 in the ratio 5:3:4

Conversion Factors

Conversion Factors are a very powerful tool for dealing with a wide variety of questions and the method is very easy.

Method

1) Find the Conversion Factor (always easy)
2) Multiply by it AND divide by it
3) Choose the common sense answer

Three Important Examples

1) *"Convert 2.55 hours into minutes."* (This is NOT 2hrs 55mins)

1) Conversion factor = 60 — (simply because 1 hour = 60 mins)
2) 2.55 hrs × 60 = 153 mins (makes sense)
   2.55 hrs ÷ 60 = 0.0425 mins (ridiculous answer!)
3) So plainly the answer is that 2.55hrs = 153 mins (=2hrs 33mins)

2) *"If £1 = 7.75 French Francs, how much is 47.36 Francs in £ and p?"*

1) Obviously, Conversion Factor = 7.75 (The "exchange rate")
2) 47.36 × 7.75 = £367.04
   47.36 ÷ 7.75 = £6.11
3) Not quite so obvious this time, but if roughly 8 Francs = £1, then 47 Francs can't be much — certainly not £367, so the answer must be £6.11p

3) *"A map has a scale of 1:20,000. How big in real life is a distance of 3cm on the map?"*

1) Conversion Factor = 20 000
2) 3cm × 20 000 = 60 000cm (looks OK)
   3cm ÷ 20 000 = 0.00015cm (not good)
3) So 60,000cm is the answer.
   How do we convert to metres?

To Convert 60,000cm to m:

1) C.F. = 100 (cm ⟷ m)
2) 60,000 × 100 = 6,000,000m (hmm)
   60,000 ÷ 100 = 600m (more like it)
3) So answer = 600m

The Acid Test:

LEARN the 3 steps of the Conversion Factor method. Then turn over and write them down.

1) Convert 2.3km into metres.
2) Which is more, £34 or 260 French Francs? (Use 7.75)
3) A map is drawn to a scale of 2cm = 5km. A road is 8 km long. How many cm will this be on the map? (Hint, C.F. = 5÷2, i.e. 1 cm = 2.5 km)

Proportion

These questions are all about two amounts that are linked together. If one amount changes, you can work out what the new value is for the other amount. The Golden Rule is to Work Out One. Once you know the amount of one thing, it's easy to work out any amount.

Lots of these questions involve money. Usually, you can Work Out One by dividing by the cost. Then multiply to find the new amount.

Here's an example with easy numbers.

Example: 4 pens cost 40p. How much would 9 pens cost?

Answer: 90p. Did you work that out straight away? What you probably said to yourself was "If 4 pens cost 40p, then 1 pen costs 10p, so 9 will cost 90p."

That's what Work Out One means — in this case, work out the cost of one pen.

Here's another example with slightly harder numbers.

Example: A shop assistant earns £7 for 2 hours work.
How much would she earn if she worked for 5 hours?

Answer: Work Out One: £7 ÷ 2 hours = £3.50 pounds for one hour.
And so the pay for 5 hours is 5 × £3.50 = £17.50

Food that is sold by weight is another situation that involves proportion.

Example: 3.5 kg of bananas cost £2.80.
How much would 5.5kg of bananas cost?

Answer: Work Out One: £2.80 ÷ 3.5 = £0.80 for 1 kg of bananas.
So for 5.5 kg you would pay 5.5 x £0.80 = £4.40

Proportion also crops up in recipes.

Example: A recipe says that you need 200g for 10 scones.
How many scones could I make if I have got 450g of flour (and plenty of the other ingredients)?

Answer: Work Out One: 200g ÷ 10 = 20g for one scone.
With 450g of flour I can make 450 ÷ 20 = 22.5 scones.
So that's 22 scones (plus a bit of flour left over).

The Acid Test:

1) What's the golden rule for proportion questions?

2) 2 kg of grapes cost £4.60. How much would 3.5 kg of grapes cost?

Standard Index Form

Standard Form and Standard Index Form are the SAME THING.
So remember both of these names as well as what it actually is:

Ordinary Number: 4,300,000 In Standard Form: 4.3×10^6

Standard form is only really useful for writing VERY BIG or VERY SMALL numbers in a more convenient way, e.g.

56,000,000,000 would be 5.6×10^{10} in standard form.
0.000 000 003 45 would be 3.45×10^{-9} in standard form.

but ANY NUMBER can be written in standard form and *you need to know how to do it*:

What it Actually is:

A number written in standard form must ALWAYS be in EXACTLY this form:

$$A \times 10^n$$

This *number* must *always* be BETWEEN 1 AND 10.
(The fancy way of saying this is: "$1 \leqslant A < 10$" — they sometimes write that in Exam questions — don't let it put you off, just remember what it means).

This number is just the NUMBER OF PLACES *the Decimal Point moves*.

Learn The Three Rules:

1) The front number must always be BETWEEN 1 AND 10
2) The power of 10, n, is purely: HOW FAR THE D.P. MOVES
3) n is +ve for BIG numbers, n is –ve for SMALL numbers

(This is much better than rules based on which way the D.P. moves.)

Examples:

1) *"Express 35 600 in standard form".*

METHOD:

1) Move the D.P. until 35 600 becomes 3.56 ("$1 \leqslant A < 10$")
2) The D.P. has moved 4 places so n=4, giving: 10^4
3) 35600 is a BIG number so n is +4, not –4

ANSWER:

3.5600. = 3.56×10^4

2) *"Express 8.14×10^{-3} as an ordinary number".*

METHOD:

1) 10^{-3}, tells us that the D.P. must move 3 places...
2) ...and the "–" sign tells us to move the D.P. to make it a SMALL number. (i.e. 0.00814, rather than 8140)

ANSWER:

8.14 = 0.00814

Also in module 5:

Standard Index Form

Standard Form and The Calculator

People usually manage all that stuff about moving the decimal point OK *(apart from always forgetting that FOR A BIG NUMBER it's "ten to the power +ve something" and FOR A SMALL NUMBER it's "ten to the power –ve something")*, but when it comes to doing standard form on a *calculator* it's invariably a sorry saga of confusion and ineptitude.

1) Entering Standard Form Numbers EXP

The button you MUST USE to put standard form numbers into the calculator is the EXP (or EE) button — but DON'T go pressing X 10 as well, like a lot of people do, because that makes it WRONG

Example: *"Enter 2.67×10^{15} into the calculator"*

Just press: 2.67 EXP 15 = and the display will be 2.67 ^{15}

Note that you ONLY PRESS the EXP (or EE) button — you DON'T press X or 10 at all.

2) Reading Standard Form Numbers:

The big thing you have to remember when you write any standard form number from the calculator display is to put the "×10" in yourself. DON'T just write down what it says on the display.

Example: *"Write down the number* 7.986 ^{05} *as a finished answer."*

As a finished answer this must be written as 7.986×10^5.

It is NOT 7.986^5 so DON'T write it down like that — YOU have to put the $\times 10^n$ in yourself, even though it isn't shown in the display at all. *That's the bit people forget.*

Adding and Subtracting

1) Change to ordinary numbers.
2) Do the adding or subtracting as normal.
3) Change your answer back to standard form.

Example: *"Work out $2 \times 10^3 + 4 \times 10^5$"*

$2 \times 10^3 = 2000$, $4 \times 10^5 = 400000$
$2000 + 400000 = 402000$

$402000 = 4.02 \times 10^5$

Multiplying and Dividing

1) Multiply or divide the two front numbers.
2) If you are multiplying — add the powers.
   If you are dividing — subtract the powers.
3) Check that your number is still in standard form — make sure the front number is between 1 and 10.

Example: *"Work out $8 \times 10^7 \div 2 \times 10^4$"*

$8 \div 2 = 4$ and $10^7 \div 10^4 = 10^3$

So answer is 4×10^3

The Acid Test:

LEARN the Three Rules and the Two Calculator Methods, then turn over and write them down.

1) Express 958,000 and 0.00018 in standard index form.
2) Work out $3 \times 10^4 - 3 \times 10^3$.
3) Work out $4 \times 10^4 \times 3 \times 10^5$.

Also in module 5:

Rounding Off

There are *two different ways* of specifying *where* a number should be *rounded off*. They are: "Decimal Places" and "Significant Figures". Doing "Decimal Places" is easier.

The question might say "... to 5 DECIMAL PLACES", or "... to 4 SIGNIFICANT FIGURES". Don't worry, these are just different ways of *setting the position* of the *LAST DIGIT*. Whichever way is used, the *basic method* is *always the same* and is *shown below*:

The Basic Method Has Three Steps

1) Identify the position of the LAST DIGIT.

2) Then look at the next digit to the RIGHT — called the DECIDER.

3) If the DECIDER is 5 or more, then ROUND-UP the LAST DIGIT.
   If the DECIDER is 4 or less, then leave the LAST DIGIT as it is.

EXAMPLE: *"What is 7.45839 to 2 Decimal Places?"*

7.45839 = **7.46**

LAST DIGIT to be written (2nd decimal place because we're rounding to 2 d.p.) — the 5

DECIDER — the 8

The *LAST DIGIT* rounds *UP* because the *DECIDER* is *5 or more*

Decimal Places (D.P)

This is pretty easy:

1) To round off to, say, 4 decimal places, the *LAST DIGIT* will be the *4th one after the decimal point*.
2) There must be *no more digits* after the LAST DIGIT (not even zeros).

DECIMAL PLACES EXAMPLES

Original number: 45.319461

Rounded to 5 decimal places (5 d.p.) 45.31946 (DECIDER was 1, so don't round up)
Rounded to 4 decimal places (4 d.p.) 45.3195 (DECIDER was 6, so do round up)
Rounded to 3 decimal places (3 d.p.) 45.319 (DECIDER was 4, so don't round up)
Rounded to 2 decimal places (2 d.p.) 45.32 (DECIDER was 9, so do round up)

The Acid Test:

LEARN the 3 Steps of the Basic Method and the 2 Extra Points for Decimal Places.

Now turn over and write down what you've learned. Then try again till you know it.

1) Round 3.5743 to 2 decimal places
2) Give 0.0481 to 2 decimal places
3) Express 12.9096 to 3 d.p.
4) Express 3546.054 to 1 d.p.

Rounding Off

Significant Figures (Sig. Fig.)

The method for sig. fig. is *identical* to that for d.p. except that finding the *position* of the *LAST DIGIT* is more difficult — it wouldn't be so bad, but for the ZEROS ...

1) The 1st significant figure of any number is simply THE FIRST DIGIT WHICH ISN'T A ZERO.

2) The 2nd, 3rd, 4th, etc. significant figures follow on immediately after the 1st, REGARDLESS OF BEING ZEROS OR NOT ZEROS.

e.g 0.002309 — *SIG FIGS:* 1st 2nd 3rd 4th

2.03070 — 1st 2nd 3rd 4th

(If we're rounding to say, 3 sig. fig. then the LAST DIGIT is simply the 3rd sig. fig.)

3) After *Rounding Off* the LAST DIGIT, end ZEROS must be filled in up to, BUT NOT BEYOND, the decimal point.

No *extra zeros* must ever be put in *after* the decimal point.

Examples	to 4 SF	to 3 SF	to 2 SF	to 1 SF
1) 54.7651	54.77	54.8	55	50
2) 17.0067	17.01	17.0	17	20
3) 0.0045902	0.004590	0.00459	0.0046	0.005
4) 30895.4	30900	30900	31000	30000

Also in module 5:

POSSIBLE ERROR OF HALF A UNIT WHEN ROUNDING

Whenever a measurement is *rounded off* to a *given UNIT* the *actual measurement* can be anything up to HALF A UNIT bigger or smaller.

Examples:

1) A room is given as being *"9m long to the nearest METRE"* — its actual length could be anything from 8.5m to 9.5m — i.e. HALF A METRE either side of 9m.

2) If it was given as *"9.4m, to the nearest 0.2m"*, then it could be anything from 9.3m to 9.5m — i.e. *0.1m either side* of 9.4m.

3) *"A school has 460 pupils to 2 Sig Fig"* (i.e. to the nearest 10) — the actual figure could be anything from 455 to 464. — (Why isn't it 465?)

The Acid Test:

LEARN the whole of this page, then turn over and write down everything you've learned. It's all good clean fun.

1) Round these to 2 d.p.: a) 3.408 b) 1.051 c) 0.068 d) 3.596

2) Round these to 3 S.F. and for each one say which of the 3 rules about ZEROS applies: a) 567.78 b) 23445 c) 0.04563 d) 0.90876

3) A car is described as 17 feet long to the nearest foot. What is the longest and shortest it could be, in feet and inches? (e.g. 14 feet 4 inches)

Accuracy and Estimating

Appropriate Accuracy

In the Exam you may well get a question asking for *"an appropriate degree of accuracy"* for a certain measurement.

So how do you decide what is *appropriate accuracy*? The key to this is *the number of significant figures* (See P.36) that you give it to, and these are the simple rules:

1) For fairly casual measurements, 2 SIGNIFICANT FIGURES is most appropriate.

EXAMPLES:

COOKING — 250 g (2 sig. fig.) of sugar,
(*not* 253 g (3 S.F.), or 300 g (1 S.F.))

DISTANCE OF A JOURNEY — 450 miles or 25 miles or 3500 miles (All 2 S.F.)

AREA OF A GARDEN OR FLOOR — 330 m^2 or 15 m^2

2) For MORE IMPORTANT OR TECHNICAL THINGS, 3 SIGNIFICANT FIGURES is essential.

EXAMPLES:

A LENGTH that will be CUT TO FIT, e.g. You'd measure a shelf as 25.6cm long
(*not 26cm or 25.63cm)*

A TECHNICAL FIGURE, e.g. 34.2 miles per gallon,
(rather than 34 mpg)

Any ACCURATE measurement with a ruler: e.g. 67.5cm, *(not 70cm or 67.54cm)*

3) Only for REALLY SCIENTIFIC WORK would you have more than 3 SIG FIG.

For example, only someone *really keen* would want to know the length of a piece of string *to the nearest tenth of a mm* — like 34.46cm, for example. *(Get a life!)*

Also in module 5:

Estimating Calculations

As long as you realise what's expected, this is *VERY EASY*. People get confused because they *over-complicate it*. To *estimate* something this is all you do:

1) ROUND EVERYTHING OFF to nice easy CONVENIENT NUMBERS.
2) Then WORK OUT THE ANSWER using those nice easy numbers — and that's it!

You don't worry about the answer being "wrong", because we're only trying to get a rough idea of the size of the proper answer, e.g. is it about 20 or about 200?

Don't forget though, in the Exam you'll need to *show all the steps you've done*, to prove you didn't just use a calculator.

Example: Q: ESTIMATE the value of $\frac{127.8 + 41.9}{56.5 \times 3.2}$ *showing all your working.*

ANSWER:

$$\frac{127.8+41.9}{56.5\times3.2} \approx \frac{130+40}{60\times3} \approx \frac{170}{180} \approx 1$$

("≈" means *"roughly equal to"*)

Calculator Buttons 1

The next few pages are full of lovely calculator tricks to save you a lot of button-bashing. There's basically two types of calculator — the old-style and the new fancy two-line displayers.

The Old-Style Calculators:

These ones only display numbers. They do the calculation each time you press an operation key.

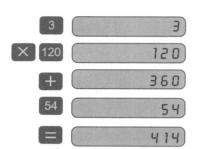

Keys	Display
3	3
× 120	120
+	360
54	54
=	414

C SEMI-CANCEL and AC ALL CANCEL

The C button only cancels the NUMBER YOU ARE ENTERING.

AC clears the whole calculation.

If you use C instead of AC for when you hit the wrong key, you'll HALVE the time you spend correcting mistakes!

2-line Display Calculators:

These fancy ones are dead common now. They're pretty easy to use because you just type most calculations exactly as they're written. Like this:

3 × 120 + 54

Display: 3 × 120 + 54

=

Display: 3 × 120 + 54
414

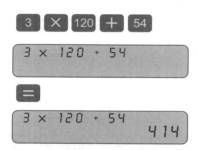

DEL The Delete button

Pressing the DEL button deletes what you've typed, one key at a time (just like on a computer), so it's much quicker than pressing AC and re-typing the whole lot. Use DEL or you'll be in BIG TROUBLE!

Cursor buttons ◀ ▶

These cursor buttons ◀ and ▶ are pretty useful for editing what you've typed in. (You'll probably find you overwrite what was there before, but you can change this with the INS key to insert, rather than overwrite.)

1) Entering Negative Numbers

On some calculators, there's a +/– button. To enter a minus number, you need to press this after you've entered the number. A lot of calculators just have a minus button (–) which you press before entering the number.

So to work out – 5 × – 6 you'd either press... (–) 5 × (–) 6 =

or... 5 +/– × 6 +/– =

Why can't they all just be the same...
(The examples in this book will use the (–) button, but if yours is different make sure you know how to use it!)

Calculator Buttons 2

2) Square, Square Root and Cube Root

The SQUARE, SQUARE ROOT, and CUBE ROOT buttons are [x^2] [$\sqrt{\ }$] and [$\sqrt[3]{\ }$].

1) The [x^2] button squares the number you typed, i.e. IT MULTIPLIES IT BY ITSELF.
It's ideal for finding the area of a circle, using the well-known (hah!) formula:
$A = \pi r^2$ e.g. if r = 5 then press [3.14] [×] [5] [x^2] [=] which gives you 78.5.
(To get a more accurate answer, use the π button which is usually the second function of the EXP key)

2) [$\sqrt{\ }$] is the REVERSE PROCESS of [x^2] — it calculates the SQUARE ROOT of the number you enter. Pressing [$\sqrt{\ }$] [25] [=] gives [5].
then [x^2] [=] takes you back to [25].

3) [$\sqrt[3]{\ }$] gives the CUBE ROOT (See P.20) which is the reverse of CUBING a number.
E.g. [$\sqrt[3]{\ }$] [27] [=] gives [3].
then pressing [x^3] [=] takes you back to [27].

3) Older Calculators do stuff Backwards

On some calculators, especially older ones, you need to enter a lot of calculations *backwards*. E.g. if you're working out the square root of a number, you'd enter the number first and then press the square root.

[25] [$\sqrt{\ }$]   [5]

Or if you were typing a trigonometry function like sin 45°, you'd do:

[45] [SIN]   [0.70716718]

You don't need to press equals when you do functions on one of these calculators. It'll work it out automatically. Which is jolly nice of it.

4) The MEMORY BUTTONS ([STO] Store, [RCL] Recall)

(On some calculators the memory buttons are called [Min] (memory in) and [MR] (memory recall)).

Contrary to popular belief, the memory is not intended for storing your favourite phone number, but in fact is a mighty useful feature for keeping a number you've just calculated, so you can use it again shortly afterwards.

For something like $\frac{16}{15+12\text{SIN}40}$, you could just work out the *bottom line* first and *stick it in the memory*:

Press [15] [+] [12] [SIN] [40] [=] and then [STO] (Or [STO] [M] or [STO] [1] or [Min])
to keep the result of the bottom line in the memory.
Then you simply press [16] [÷] [RCL] [=], and the answer is 0.7044.
(Instead of [RCL], you might need to type [RCL] [M] or [RCL] [1] or [MR] on yours.)

Once you've practised with the memory buttons a bit, you'll soon find them very useful. They can speed things up no end.

Calculator Buttons 3

5) Bodmas and the Brackets Buttons

The BRACKETS BUTTONS are (and).

One of the biggest problems people have with their calculators is not realising that the calculator always works things out IN A CERTAIN ORDER, which is summarised by the word BODMAS, which stands for:

Brackets, Other, Division, Multiplication, Addition, Subtraction

This becomes really important when you want to work out even a simple thing like $\frac{23+45}{64\times 3}$ — it's no good just pressing 23 + 45 ÷ 64 × 3 = — it will be *completely wrong*. The calculator will think you mean $23+\frac{45}{64}\times 3$ because the calculator will do the *division and multiplication* BEFORE it does the *addition*.

The secret is to OVERRIDE the automatic BODMAS order of operations using the BRACKETS BUTTONS. Brackets are the ultimate priority in BODMAS, which means anything in brackets is worked out before anything else happens to it.
So all you have to do is

1) Write a couple of pairs of brackets into the expression: $\frac{(23+45)}{(64\times 3)}$

2) Then just type it as it's written:

(23 + 45) ÷ (64 × 3) =

You might think it's difficult to know where to put the brackets in.
It's not that difficult, you just put them in pairs around each group of numbers.
It's OK to have brackets within other brackets too, e.g. (4 + (5÷2))
As a rule, you can't cause trouble by putting too many brackets in,
SO LONG AS THEY ALWAYS GO IN PAIRS.

6) The Fraction Button: $a^{b}/_{c}$

— It's absolutely essential that you learn how to use this button for doing fractions. Full details are given on P.25.

7) The Powers Button: x^y

It's used for working out powers of numbers quickly. For example to find 7^5, instead of pressing 7×7×7×7×7 you should just press 7 x^y 5 =

Calculator Buttons 4

8) The Standard Form Button

The STANDARD FORM BUTTON is EXP or EE.

All you ever use this for is entering numbers written in *standard form* into the calculator.

It would be a lot more helpful if the calculator manufacturers labelled it as $\times 10^n$ because that's what you should call it as you press it: "*Times ten to the power*..."

For example to enter 6×10^3 YOU MUST ONLY PRESS: 6 EXP 3

and NOT, as a lot of people do: 6 × 10 EXP 3 .

The calculator would then display this number as: 6^3

(REMEMBER — it doesn't mean 6^3 but 6×10^3)

Pressing × 10 as well as EXP is HORRIBLY WRONG, because the EXP ALREADY CONTAINS the "× 10" in it. That's why you should always say to yourself "TIMES TEN TO THE POWER..." every time you press the EXP button, to prevent this very common mistake.

9) Modes

This is tricky and you wouldn't really need to know about it except that you'll sometimes accidentally get into the wrong mode, and it can make life pretty difficult if you don't know how to get back to normality.

There are 3 SEPARATE MODES that your calculator has to make a choice about:

CALCULATION MODES

You want COMP mode. This is the mode for doing normal calculations.
On CASIOs, this is on the first menu you get from pressing MODE

ANGLES MODES

You want degrees mode (there'll be a small DEG or D on the display when you're in this mode).
On CASIOs, you'd press MODE twice to get the right menu.

DISPLAY MODES

You want NORM mode most of the time. The other display modes are for showing a certain number of decimals places (FIX) or number of significant figures (SCI).
(have a play with these — they're great fun... err, I mean they might be useful... or something.)

The Acid Test:

LEARN YOUR CALCULATOR BUTTONS.
PRACTISE until you can do all of these without having to refer back:

1) What do the x^2 and $\sqrt{\ }$ buttons do?

2) What must you press to find 17^2?

3) How do you enter -5×-8?

4) Explain what STO and RCL do and give an example of using them.

5) What is the $a^b/_c$ button used for?

6) How do you enter 6^8?

7) How do you enter 6×10^8?

8) Which should be showing at the top of your display: DEG, RAD or GRAD?

Revision Test for Module Three

I know these questions seem difficult, *but they're the very best revision you can do*. The whole point of revision, remember, is to find out what you *don't* know and then learn it until you do. These searching questions test how much you know *better than anything else ever can*. They follow the sequence of pages in Module Three, so you can easily look up anything you don't know.

Keep learning these basic facts until you know them

1) What are the multiples of a number? What are the factors of a number?
2) What is the best method for finding all the factors of a number?
3) What are the prime factors of a number? How do you find them?
4) Explain exactly what HCF and LCM mean.
5) State the two rules for finding Prime numbers (below 120).
6) What are the 3 rules for combining powers?
7) What are the other 4 rules for powers?
8) Explain what the square root of a number is. Explain what the cube root is.
9) Give a rule for negative numbers and say when it should be used.
10) Give an example of a fraction that divides to give a terminating decimal. And one that doesn't.
11) What does FDP stand for? Give full details of the four conversion methods.
12) Describe in words the 5 rules for doing fractions by hand.
13) Order these fractions by their size, smallest first: $^{13}/_{128}$, $^{7}/_{64}$, $^{4}/_{32}$, $^{121}/_{128}$, $^{15}/_{16}$.
14) Which is the fraction button? What must you press to enter $2\frac{3}{4}$?
15) How would you convert it to a top heavy fraction?
16) Describe the 3 types of percentage question and how to identify them.
17) Give details of the method for each of the 3 types of percentage question.
18) Give the formula for percentage change, and give 3 examples of it.
19) What is the formula for compound growth and decay?
20) Give three important examples to show how the method is always the same.
21) Which two things can a ratio be converted into?
22) Which calculator button can you use to simplify ratios?
23) What is the formula triangle for ratios?
24) State the 3 steps of the method for applying conversion factors.
25) What is the general format of a number expressed in standard form?
26) What are the three rules for expressing a number in standard form?
27) What are the three steps for rounding off?
28) What are the 3 extra details concerning sig. fig. rounding?
29) State two rules for estimating the answer to a calculation.
30) Which are the memory buttons on your calculator? What are they used for?
31) What does BODMAS mean and what has it got to do with your calculator?
32) When would you use the brackets buttons?
33) Which is the powers button? What must you press to find 8^{15}?
34) Which is the Standard Form button? What must you press to enter 3×10^{-4}?
35) What would the number 5×10^{7} look like on the calculator display?
36) Which 3 modes should your calculator be in?

Special Number Sequences

1) EVEN NUMBERS ...all Divide by 2

2 4 6 8 10 12 14 16 18 20 ...

All *EVEN* numbers **END** in 0, 2, 4, 6 or 8

e.g. 200, 342, 576, 94

2) ODD NUMBERS ...DON'T divide by 2

1 3 5 7 9 11 13 15 17 19 ...

All *ODD* numbers **END** in 1, 3, 5, 7 or 9

e.g. 301, 95, 807, 43

3) POWERS

Powers are "numbers *multiplied by themselves* so many times".

"*Two to the power three*" $= 2^3 = 2 \times 2 \times 2 = 8$

Here's the first few *POWERS OF 2*:

2 4 8 16 32 ...

$2^1=2$ $2^2=4$ $2^3=8$ $2^4=16$ etc...

... and the first *POWERS OF 10* (even easier):

10 100 1000 10 000 ...

$10^1=10$ $10^2=100$ $10^3=1000$ etc...

4) TRIANGLE NUMBERS

To remember the triangle numbers you have to picture in your mind this *increasing pattern of triangles*, where each new row has *one more blob* than the previous row.

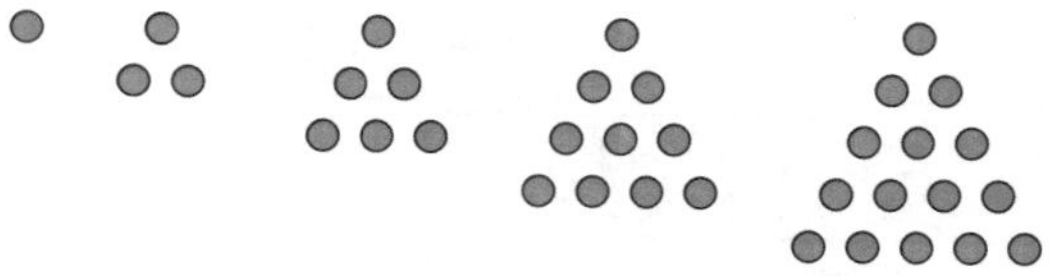

1 3 6 10 15 21 28 36 45 55 ....

2 3 4 5 6 7 8 9 10 11 12

It's definitely worth learning this simple *pattern of differences*, as well as the formula for the nth term (see p.44).

5) MULTIPLES

The multiples of 3 are: 3, 6, 9, 12, 15, ...

This number pattern starts at 3 and goes up in 3s.
The formula for the multiples of 3 is 3n.
The general formula for the multiples of the number **a** is **a**n.

See P.16 for a reminder about multiples.

Making other sequences from multiples:

Example: 5, 8, 11, 14, 17, ...

This sequence goes up in 3s just like the multiples of 3.
To get from the multiples of 3 to this sequence you have to add 2 each time:

3	6	9	12	15	...
+2	+2	+2	+2	+2	...
5	8	11	14	17	...

So the nth term for the sequence 5, 8, 11, 14, 17, ... is $3n + 2$.

Example: 2, 7, 12, 17, 22, ...

This sequence goes up in 5s, so it is like the multiples of 5.
To get from the multiples of 5 to this sequence you have to subtract 3.

5	10	15	20	25	...
-3	-3	-3	-3	-3	...
2	7	12	17	22	...

So the nth term for the sequence 2, 7, 12, 17, 22, ... is $5n - 3$.

The Acid Test:

1) Cover up the page and then write down the first 15 numbers in all of the sequences above.
2) From this list of numbers: 23, 45, 56, 81, 25, 97, 134, 156, 125, 36, 1, 64
   write down: a) all the even numbers b) all the odd numbers
   c) all the powers of 2 and 10. d) all the triangle numbers.
3) Write down the formula for the nth term of the sequence: 4, 10, 16, 22, 28, ...

Finding the nth Term

"The nth term" is a formula with "n" in it which gives you every term in a sequence when you put different values for n in. There are two different types of sequence (for "nth term" questions) which have to be done in different ways:

Common Difference Type: "dn + (a – d)"

For any sequence such as 3, 7, 11, 15, where there's a COMMON DIFFERENCE:

(differences: 4, 4, 4)

you can always find "the nth term" using the FORMULA: **n^{th} Term = dn+(a–d)**

Don't forget:

1) "a" is simply the value of THE FIRST TERM in the sequence.
2) "d" is simply the value of THE COMMON DIFFERENCE between the terms.
3) To get the nth term, you just find the values of "a" and "d" from the sequence and stick them in the formula.
   You don't replace n though — that wants to stay as n
4) Of course YOU HAVE TO LEARN THE FORMULA, but life is like that.

Example:

"Find the nth term of this sequence: 5, 8, 11, 14, ..."

ANSWER:
1) The formula is dn + (a – d)
2) The first term is 5, so a = 5 — The common difference is 3 so d = 3
3) Putting these in the formula gives: n^{th} term = 3n + (5 – 3)
   so n^{th} term = 3n + 2

Changing Difference Type:

"a + (n–1)d + ½(n–1)(n–2)C"

If the number sequence is one where the *difference* between the terms is *increasing or decreasing* then it gets a whole lot more complicated (as you'll have spotted from the above formula — which you'll have to *learn*!). This time there are *THREE* letters you have to fill in:

"a" is the FIRST TERM,
"d" is the FIRST DIFFERENCE (between the first two numbers),
"C" is the CHANGE BETWEEN ONE DIFFERENCE AND THE NEXT.

Example:

"Find the nth term of this sequence: 2, 5, 9, 14, ..."

(differences: 3, 4, 5)

ANSWER:
1) The formula is *"a + (n–1)d + ½(n–1)(n–2)C"*
2) The first term is 2, so a = 2 — The first difference is 3 so d = 3
3) The differences increase by 1 each time so C = +1

Putting these in the formula gives: *"2 + (n–1)3 + ½(n–1)(n–2)×1"*
Which becomes: $2 + 3n - 3 + \frac{1}{2}n^2 - 1\frac{1}{2}n + 1$
Which simplifies to: $\frac{1}{2}n^2 + 1\frac{1}{2}n = \frac{1}{2}n(n+3)$
so the nth term = ½n(n+3)

(Easy peasy, huh!)

The Acid Test:

LEARN the definition of the nth term and the 4 steps for finding it, and LEARN THE FORMULA.

1) Find the nth term of the following sequences:
a) 4, 7, 10, 13,.... b) 3, 8, 13, 18,.... c) 1, 3, 6, 10, 15,.... d) 3, 4, 7, 12,...

Basic Algebra

1) Terms

Before you can do anything else, you MUST understand what a TERM is:

1) **A TERM IS A COLLECTION OF NUMBERS, LETTERS AND BRACKETS, ALL MULTIPLIED/DIVIDED TOGETHER.**

2) TERMS are SEPARATED BY + AND – SIGNS. e.g. $4x^2 - 3py - 5 + 3p$

3) TERMS always have a + or – ATTACHED TO THE FRONT OF THEM.

4) e.g. $4xy + 5x^2 - 2y + 6y^2 + 4$

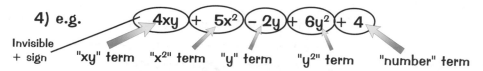

Invisible + sign — "xy" term — "x^2" term — "y" term — "y^2" term — "number" term

5) An EXPRESSION is a bunch of terms joined together.

6) An EQUATION is an expression with an EQUALS SIGN in it,

e.g. $3x^2 + 5x - 7$ is an expression,
$3x^2 + 5x - 7 = 2x + 1$ is an equation.

2) Simplifying

"Collecting Like Terms"

EXAMPLE: *"Simplify $2x - 4 + 5x + 6$"*

$2x\ -4\ +5x\ +6 \;=\; +2x\ +5x\ -4\ +6$

x-terms — number terms $\;=\; 7x\ \ +2 \;=\; 7X + 2$

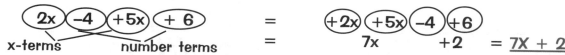

1) Put bubbles round each term — be sure you capture the +/– sign in front of each.
2) Then you can move the bubbles into the best order so that like terms are together.
3) "Like terms" have exactly the same combination of letters, e.g. "x-terms" or "xy-terms".
4) Combine like terms using the number line.

3) Letters Multiplied Together

This is the super-slick notation they like to use in algebra which just ends up making life difficult for folks like you. You've got to remember these five rules:

1) "abc" means "$a \times b \times c$" — The ×'s are often left out to make it clearer.
2) "gn^2" means "$g \times n \times n$" — Note that only the n is squared, not the g as well.
3) "$(gn)^2$" means "$g \times g \times n \times n$" — The brackets mean that BOTH letters are squared.
4) "$p(q - r)^3$" means "$p \times (q - r) \times (q - r) \times (q - r)$" — Only the brackets get cubed.
5) "-3^2" is too ambiguous. — It should either be written $(-3)^2 = 9$, or $-(3^2) = -9$.

Basic Algebra

4) Multiplying out Brackets

1) The thing OUTSIDE the brackets multiplies each separate term INSIDE the brackets.
2) When letters are multiplied together, they are just written next to each other, pq.
3) Remember, $R \times R = R^2$, and TY^2 means $T\times Y\times Y$, whilst $(TY)^2$ means $T\times T\times Y\times Y$.
4) Remember a minus outside the bracket REVERSES ALL THE SIGNS when you multiply.

Examples: 1) $3(2x + 5) = 6x + 15$ 2) $4p(3r - 2t) = 12pr - 8pt$

3) $-4(3p^2 - 7q^3) = -12p^2 + 28q^3$ (note both signs have been *reversed* — Rule 4)

5) Cancelling Algebraic Fractions

This is exactly the same as cancelling ordinary fractions.

1) Look for any bits that look the same (common factors) that are on both the top and the bottom.
2) Cancel them.

Examples: 1) Simplify: $\frac{2x(x-1)}{(x-1)}$ Answer: $\frac{2x\cancel{(x-1)}}{\cancel{(x-1)}} = 2x$

Cross out each term that's on both the top and the bottom.

2) Simplify: $\frac{6x(x+4)(x-1)}{3x(x-1)}$ Answer: $\frac{\overset{2}{\cancel{6x}}(x+4)\cancel{(x-1)}}{\cancel{3x}\cancel{(x-1)}} = 2(x+4)$

6) Expanding and Simplifying

a) With DOUBLE BRACKETS

— you get 4 terms after multiplying them out and usually 2 of them combine to leave 3 terms, like this:

$$(2P - 4)(3P + 1) = (2P \times 3P) + (2P \times 1) + (-4 \times 3P) + (-4 \times 1)$$
$$= 6P^2 + 2P - 12P - 4$$
$$= 6P^2 - 10P - 4$$

(these 2 combine together)

b) SQUARED BRACKETS:

e.g. $(3d + 5)^2$ ALWAYS write these out as two brackets: $(3d + 5)(3d + 5)$ and work them out CAREFULLY like this:

$$(3d + 5)(3d + 5) = 9d^2 + 15d + 15d + 25 = 9d^2 + 30d + 25$$

YOU SHOULD ALWAYS GET FOUR TERMS from squared brackets, and inevitably *two of these* will combine together to leave THREE TERMS IN THE END, as shown above.

(The usual WRONG ANSWER, by the way, is $(3d + 5)^2 = 9d^2 + 25$ — eeek!)

Basic Algebra

7) Factorising — putting brackets in

This is the *exact reverse* of multiplying-out brackets. Here's the method to follow:

1) Take out the biggest NUMBER that goes into all the terms.
2) Take each letter in turn and take out the highest power (e.g. x, x^2 etc.) that will go into EVERY term.
3) Open the brackets and fill in all the bits needed to reproduce each term.

EXAMPLE: Factorise $15x^4y + 20x^2y^3z - 35x^3yz^2$

Answer: $5x^2y(3x^2 + 4y^2z - 7xz^2)$

Biggest number that'll divide into 15, 20 and 35

Highest powers of X and Y that will go into all three terms

Z wasn't in ALL terms so it can't come out as a common factor

REMEMBER:

1) The bits *taken out and put at the front* are the *COMMON FACTORS*.
2) The bits *inside the brackets* are *what's needed to get back to the original terms* if you were to multiply the brackets out again.

D.O.T.S. — The Difference Of Two Squares:

$$a^2 - b^2 = (a + b)(a - b)$$

The "difference of two squares" (D.O.T.S. for short) is where you have "one thing squared" minus "another thing squared". In the Exam you're likely to be asked to factorise a D.O.T.S. expression (i.e. put it into two brackets as above). People mess this up because they haven't made enough effort to learn it. Best do it now, eh, before it's too late.
Make sure you LEARN this example:

Factorise $x^2 - 16$. Answer: $x^2 - 16 = (x + 4)(x - 4)$

The Acid Test:

LEARN the important details for each of the 7 sections on these 2 pages, then turn over and write it all down.

Then apply the methods to these:

1) Simplify: a) $5x + 3y - 4 - 2y - x$ b) $4k + 3y^2 - 6k + y^2 + 2$ c) $\frac{2(x+1)^2}{(x+1)}$
2) Expand: a) $2pq(3p - 4q^2)$ b) $(2g + 5)(4g - 2)$ c) $(4 - 3h)^2$
3) Factorise: a) $14x^2y^3 + 21xy^2 - 35x^3y^4$ b) $12h^2j^3 + 6h^4j^2k - 36h^3jk$

Solving Equations the Easy Way

The "proper" way to solve equations is shown on P.49. In practise the "proper way" can be pretty difficult so there's a lot to be said for the much easier methods shown below.

The drawback with these is that you can't always use them on very complicated equations. In most Exam questions though, they do just fine.

1) THE "COMMON SENSE" APPROACH

The trick here is to realise that the unknown quantity "X" is after all just a number and the "equation" is just a cryptic clue to help you find it.

Example: *"Solve this equation: $3X + 4 = 46$"*

(i.e. find what number X is)

Answer: *This is what you should say to yourself:*

"Something + 4 = 46" hmm, so that "something" must be 42.

So that means $3X = 42$, which means "3 times something = 42"

So it must be $42 \div 3$ which is 14 so $X = 14$ "

In other words don't think of it as algebra, but as "Find the mystery number".

2) THE TRIAL AND ERROR METHOD

This is a perfectly good method, and although it won't work every time, it usually does, especially if the answer is a *whole number*.

The *big secret of trial and error* methods is to find TWO OPPOSITE CASES and keep taking values IN BETWEEN them.

In other words, find a number that makes the RHS bigger, and then one that makes the LHS bigger, and then try values *in between them*.

Example: *"Solve for X: $3X + 5 = 21 - 5X$"*

(i.e. find the number X)

Answer:

Try X=1: $3 + 5 = 21 - 5$, $8 = 16$ — no good, RHS too big

Try X=3: $9 + 5 = 21 - 15$, $14 = 6$ — no good, now LHS too big

SO TRY IN BETWEEN: $X = 2$: $6 + 5 = 21 - 10$, $11 = 11$, YES, so $X = 2$.

The Acid Test: LEARN these two methods until you can turn the page and write them down with an example for each.

1) Solve: $4x - 12 = 20$ 2) Solve: $3x + 5 = 5x - 9$

Solving Equations

The aim of solving an equation is to work out what the letter stands for. You want to end up with an equation that says "$x = 2$" or "$p = 1.5$".

Golden Rules

1) Always do the SAME thing to both sides of the equation.
2) To get rid of something, do the opposite.
   The opposite of + is – and the opposite of – is +.
   The opposite of × is ÷ and the opposite of ÷ is ×.
3) Keep going until you have a letter on its own.

EXAMPLE 1: Solve $5x = 15$

$5x = 15$ ← $5x$ means $5 \times x$, so do the opposite — divide both sides by 5.

$x = 3$

EXAMPLE 2: Solve $^p/_3 = 2$

$p/3 = 2$ ← $^p/_3$ means $p \div 3$, so do the opposite — multiply both sides by 3.

$p = 6$

EXAMPLE 3: Solve $4y - 3 = 17$

$4y - 3 = 17$ ← The opposite of -3 is $+3$ so add 3 to both sides.

$4y = 20$ ← The opposite of $\times 4$ is $\div 4$ so divide both sides by 4.

$y = 5$

EXAMPLE 4: Solve $2(x + 3) = 11$

$2(x + 3) = 11$ ← The opposite of $\times 2$ is $\div 2$ so divide both sides by 2.

$x + 3 = 5.5$ ← The opposite of $+3$ is -3 so subtract 3 from both sides.

$x = 2.5$

If there are letters on both sides of the equation, start by getting rid of the smaller number of the letter from both sides.

EXAMPLE: Solve $3x + 5 = 5x + 1$

$3x + 5 = 5x + 1$

there are x's on both sides, so subtract $3x$ from both sides. →

$5 = 2x + 1$

the opposite of $+1$ is -1, so subtract 1 from each side. →

$4 = 2x$

the opposite of $\times 2$ is $\div 2$, so divide each side by 2. →

$2 = x$

The Acid Test

Solve these equations:

a) $3x + 1 = 13$ b) $^q/_4 = 8$

c) $2(p - 3) = 5$ d) $5y + 4 = 2y - 2$

Substituting Values into Formulas

This topic is a lot easier than you think!

$$C = \frac{5}{9}(F - 32)$$

Generally speaking, algebra is a pretty grim subject, but you should realise that some bits of it are VERY easy, and this is definitely the easiest bit of all, so whatever you do, don't pass up on these easy Exam marks.

Method

If you don't follow this STRICT METHOD you'll just keep getting them wrong — it's as simple as that.

1) Write out the formula — e.g. $F = \frac{9}{5}C + 32$

2) Write it again, directly underneath, but substituting numbers for letters on the RHS (Right Hand Side). — $F = \frac{9}{5}15 + 32$

3) Work it out IN STAGES. Use BODMAS to work things out IN THE RIGHT ORDER. WRITE DOWN values for each bit as you go along. — $F = 27 + 32$, $= 59$, $F = 59°$

4) DO NOT attempt to do it all in one go on your calculator. That ridiculous method fails at least 50% of the time!

BODMAS

Brackets, Other, Division, Multiplication, Addition, Subtraction

BODMAS tells you the ORDER in which these operations should be done: Work out brackets first, then other things like squaring, then multiply / divide groups of numbers before adding or subtracting them. This set of rules works really well for simple cases, so remember the word: BODMAS

Example

A mysterious quantity T, is given by: $T = (P - 7)^2 + 4R/Q$
Find the value of T when P = 4, Q = -2 and R = 3

ANSWER:

1) Write down the formula: $T = (P - 7)^2 + 4R/Q$
2) Put the numbers in: $T = (4 - 7)^2 + 4\times3/-2$
3) Then work it out in stages: $= (-3)^2 + 12/-2$
$= 9 + -6$
$= 9 - 6 = 3$

Note BODMAS in operation:

Brackets worked out first, then *squared*. *Multiplications* and *divisions* done *before* finally *adding* and *subtracting*.

The Acid Test:

LEARN the 4 Steps of the Substitution Method and the full meaning of BODMAS. Then turn over.....

... and write it all down from memory. 1) Practise the above example until you can do it easily without help. 2) If $C = \frac{5}{9}(F - 32)$, find the value of C when F = 77.

Rearranging Formulas

Rearranging Formulas means making one letter the subject, e.g. getting "y= " from something like 2x + z = 3(y + 2p). Generally speaking "solving equations" is easier, but don't forget:

1) EXACTLY THE SAME METHOD APPLIES TO BOTH FORMULAS AND EQUATIONS.
2) THE SAME SEQUENCE OF STEPS APPLIES EVERY TIME.

We'll illustrate this by making "y" the subject of this formula: $M = \sqrt{2K - \frac{K^2}{2y+1}}$

The Six Steps Applied to Formulas

1) Get rid of any square root signs by squaring both sides:

$$M^2 = 2K - \frac{K^2}{2y+1}$$

2) Get everything off the bottom by cross-multiplying up to EVERY OTHER TERM:

$$M^2 = 2K - \frac{K^2}{2y+1} \Rightarrow M^2(2y+1) = 2K(2y+1) - K^2$$

3) Multiply out any brackets:

$$2yM^2 + M^2 = 4Ky + 2K - K^2$$

4) Collect all subject terms on one side of the "=" and all non-subject terms on the other side, remembering to reverse the +/– sign of any term that crosses the "=":

+4Ky moves across the "=" and becomes – 4Ky
+M² moves across the "=" and becomes – M²

$$2yM^2 - 4Ky = -M^2 + 2K - K^2$$

5) Combine together like terms on each side of the equation, and reduce it to the form "Ax = B", where A and B are just bunches of letters which DON'T include the subject (y). Note that the LHS has to be FACTORISED:

$$(2M^2 - 4K)y = 2K - K^2 - M^2$$

("Ax = B" i.e. $A = (2M^2 - 4K)$, $B = 2K - K^2 - M^2$, y is the subject)

6) Finally slide the A underneath the B to give "X = B/A", (cancel if possible) and that's your answer:

So $y = \frac{2K - K^2 - M^2}{(2M^2 - 4K)}$

And One Extra Thing...

If you find yourself having to solve for a *squared coefficient* then treat it just like normal (i.e. put x^2 = a random variable, say 'P') then at the end, just take the *square root* of the other side — simple! Try and follow this example through:

Solve for x:

$$y = 3K + \frac{2x^2 - 3L}{2}$$

$$\Rightarrow y = 3K + \frac{2P - 3L}{2}$$

$$\Rightarrow P = \frac{2(y-3K)+3L}{2} = x^2 \Rightarrow x = \sqrt{\frac{2(y-3K)+3L}{2}}$$

I've missed out a load of steps here, but you should be able to work out what I did by looking through the stuff above.

The Acid Test:

LEARN the 6 STEPS for solving equations and rearranging formulas. Turn over and write them down.

1) Rearrange " $F = \frac{9}{5}C + 32$ " from "F= ", to "C= " and then back the other way.
2) Make p the subject of these: a) $\frac{p}{p+y} = 4$ b) $y = x^2p^2 - 3p^2$

Quadratics

Factorising a Quadratic

"Factorising a quadratic" means "putting it into 2 brackets" — you'll need to remember that. There are several different methods for doing this, so stick with the one you're happiest with. If you have no preference then learn this one. The standard format for any quadratic equations is: $x^2 + bx + c = 0$ (e.g. $x^2 + 3x + 2 = 0$)

Factorising Method

1) ALWAYS rearrange into the STANDARD FORMAT: $x^2 + bx + c = 0$.
2) Write down the TWO BRACKETS with the x's in: $(x \quad)(x \quad) = 0$.
3) Then find 2 numbers that MULTIPLY to give "c" (the end number) but also ADD/SUBTRACT to give "b" (the coefficient of x).
4) Put them in and check that the +/– signs work out properly.

Example

"Solve $x^2 - x = 12$ by factorising."

ANSWER: 1) First rearrange it (into the standard format): $x^2 - x - 12 = 0$

2) The initial brackets are (as ever): $(x \quad)(x \quad) = 0$

3) We now want to look at all pairs of numbers that multiply to give "c" (=12), but which also add or subtract to give the value of b: (-1)

1 × 12	*Add/subtract to give:*	13 or 11	
2 × 6	*Add/subtract to give:*	8 or 4	this is what we're after
3 × 4	*Add/subtract to give:*	7 or (1) ←	(1 is "b", within ±)

4) So 3 and 4 will give b = ±1, so put them in: $(x \quad 3)(x \quad 4) = 0$

5) Now fill in the +/– signs so that the 3 and 4 add/subtract to give -1 (=b). Clearly it must be +3 and – 4 so we'll have: $(x + 3)(x - 4) = 0$

6) As an ESSENTIAL check, EXPAND the brackets out again to make sure they give the original equation:
$(x + 3)(x - 4) = x^2 + 3x - 4x - 12 = x^2 - x - 12$

We're not finished yet mind, because $(x + 3)(x - 4) = 0$ is only the factorised form of the equation — we have yet to give the actual SOLUTIONS. This is very easy:

7) THE SOLUTIONS are simply the two numbers in the brackets, but with OPPOSITE +/– SIGNS: i.e. $x = -3$ or $+4$

Make sure you remember that last step. It's the difference between SOLVING THE EQUATION and merely factorising it.

The Acid Test:

LEARN the 7 steps for solving quadratics by factorising.

1) Solve these *by the factor method*: a) $x^2 + 5x + 6 = 0$ b) $x^2 + 8x + 12 = 0$ c) $x^2 + 5x - 24 = 0$ d) $x^2 - 6x + 9 = 16$

Trial and Improvement

In principle, this is an easy way to find approximate answers to quite complicated equations, especially "cubics" (ones with x^3 in). BUT... you have to make an effort to LEARN THE FINER DETAILS of this method, otherwise you'll never get the hang of it.

Method

1) **SUBSTITUTE TWO INITIAL VALUES into the equation that give OPPOSITE CASES.** These are usually suggested in the question. If not, you'll have to think of your own. Opposite cases means one answer too big, one too small, or one +ve, one –ve, for example. If they don't give opposite cases try again.

2) **Now CHOOSE YOUR NEXT VALUE IN BETWEEN THE PREVIOUS TWO, and SUBSTITUTE it into the equation.**
Continue this process, always choosing a new value between the two closest opposite cases, (and preferably nearer to the one which is closest to the answer you want).

3) **AFTER ONLY 3 OR 4 STEPS you should have 2 numbers which are to the right degree of accuracy but DIFFER BY 1 IN THE LAST DIGIT.**
For example if you had to get your answer to 2 DP then you'd eventually end up with say 5.43 and 5.44, with these giving OPPOSITE results of course.

4) **At this point you ALWAYS take the Exact Middle Value to decide which is the answer you want.** e.g. for 5.43 and 5.44, you'd try 5.435 to see if the real answer was between 5.43 and 5.435 or between 5.435 and 5.44 (see below).

Example

"The equation $X^3 + X = 40$ has a solution between 3 and 3.5. Find this solution to 1 DP"

Try X = 3 $3^3 + 3 = 30$ (Too small)
Try X = 3.5 $3.5^3 + 3.5 = 46.375$ (Too big) ← (2 opposite cases)

40 is what we want and it's closer to 46.375 than it is to 30 so we'll choose our next value for X closer to 3.5 than 3

Try X = 3.3 $3.3^3 + 3.3 = 39.237$ (Too small)

Good, this is very close, but we need to see if 3.4 is still too big or too small:

Try X = 3.4 $3.4^3 + 3.4 = 42.704$ (Too big)

Good, now we know that the answer must be between 3.3 and 3.4. To find out which one it's nearest to, we have to try the EXACT MIDDLE VALUE: 3.35

Try X = 3.35 $3.35^3 + 3.35 = 40.945$ (Too big)

This tells us with certainty that the solution must be between 3.3 (too small) and 3.35 (too big), and so to 1 DP it must round down to 3.3. ANSWER = 3.3

The Acid Test:

"LEARN and TURN" — if you don't actually commit it to memory, then you've wasted your time even reading it.

To succeed with this method you must LEARN the 4 steps above. Do it now, and practise until you can write them down without having to look back at them. It's not as difficult as you think.

1) The equation $X^3 - 2X = 1$ has a solution between 1 and 2. Find it to 1 DP.

Simultaneous Equations

These are OK as long as you learn these SIX STEPS in every meticulous detail.

There are Six Steps in the Solution

We'll use these two equations for this example: $2x = 6 - 4y$ and $-3 - 3y = 4x$

1) REARRANGE BOTH EQUATIONS INTO THE FORM: $ax + by = c$
where a,b,c are numbers, (which can be negative).
Also LABEL THE TWO EQUATIONS —① and —②

$2x + 4y = 6$ —①
$-4x - 3y = 3$ —②

2) You need to MATCH UP THE NUMBERS IN FRONT (the "coefficients") of either the x's or y's in BOTH EQUATIONS.
To do this you may need to MULTIPLY one or both equations by a suitable number. You should then RELABEL them: —③ and —④

①×2 : $4x + 8y = 12$ —③
$-4x - 3y = 3$ —④

(This gives us $+4x$ in equation —③ to match the $-4x$ in equation —②, now called —④)

3) ADD OR SUBTRACT THE TWO EQUATIONS ...
...to eliminate the terms with the same coefficient.
If the coefficients are the SAME (both +ve or both –ve) then SUBTRACT.
If the coefficients are OPPOSITE (one +ve and one –ve) then ADD.

③+④ $0x + 5y = 15$ (In this case we have $+4x$ and $-4x$ so we ADD)

4) SOLVE THE RESULTING EQUATION to find whichever letter is left in it.

$5y = 15 \Rightarrow y = 3$

5) SUB THIS BACK into equation ① and solve it to find the other quantity.

Sub in ①: $2x + 4\times3 = 6 \Rightarrow 2x + 12 = 6 \Rightarrow 2x = -6 \Rightarrow x = -3$

6) Then SUBSTITUTE BOTH THESE VALUES INTO EQUATION ② to make sure it works out properly. If it doesn't then you've done something wrong and you'll have to do it all again!

Sub x and y in ②: $-4\times-3 - 3\times3 = 12 - 9 = 3$
which is right, so it's worked.

So the solutions are: $x = -3$, $y = 3$

The Acid Test: LEARN the *6 Steps* for solving *Simultaneous Equations*.

Remember, you only know them when you can write them all out from memory, so turn over the page and try it. Then apply the 6 steps to find F and G given that
$2F - 10 = 4G$ and $3G = 4F - 15$

Simultaneous Equations with Graphs

On the opposite page is the *tricky algebra method* for solving simultaneous equations.
On this page is the *nice easy graph method* for solving them.
You could be asked to do *either* method in the Exam so make sure you *learn them both*.

Solving Simultaneous Equations Using Graphs

This is a very easy way to find the x- and y- solutions to two simultaneous equations.
Here's the simple rule:

THE SOLUTION OF TWO SIMULTANEOUS EQUATIONS IS SIMPLY THE X AND Y VALUES WHERE THEIR GRAPHS CROSS

Three Step Method

1) Do a *"TABLE OF 3 VALUES"* for both equations.

2) Draw the Two *GRAPHS*.

3) Find the X- and Y-values *WHERE THEY CROSS*.

Easy Peasy.

Example

"Draw the graphs for "Y = 2X + 3" and "Y = 6 – 4X" and then use your graphs to solve them."

1) TABLE OF 3 VALUES (see P.63) for both equations:

X	0	2	-2
Y	3	7	-1

X	0	2	3
Y	6	-2	-6

2) DRAW THE GRAPHS:

3) WHERE THEY CROSS, $x = ½, y = 4$. And that's the answer!

$x = ½$ and $y = 4$

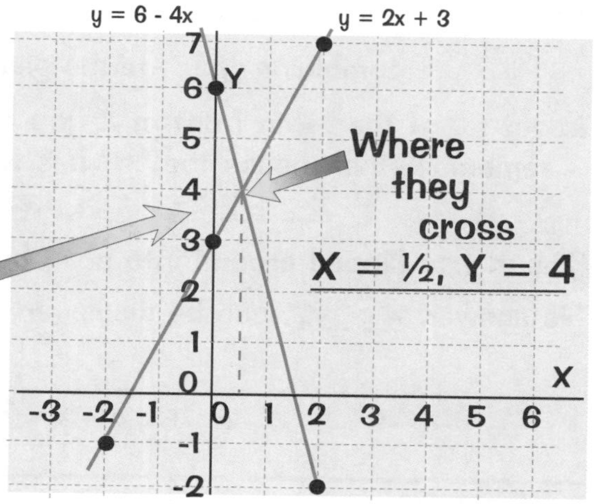

See P.58 for more on X and Y coordinates.

The Acid Test:

LEARN the Simple Rule and the 3 step method for solving simultaneous equations using GRAPHS.

1) Cover the page and write down the Simple Rule and the 3 step method.
2) Use graphs to find the solutions to these pairs of equations:
   a) $Y = 4x - 4$ and $Y = 6 - X$ b) $Y = 2x$ and $Y = 6 - 2x$

Inequalities

This is basically quite difficult, but it's still worth learning the easy bits in case they ask a very easy question on it, as well they might. Here are the easy bits:

The 4 Inequality Symbols:

$>$ means "Greater than" | $\geq$ means "Greater than or equal to"

$<$ means "Less than" | $\leq$ means "Less than or equal to"

REMEMBER, the one at the BIG end is BIGGEST

so "$X > 4$" and "$4 < X$" *BOTH* say: "X is greater than 4"

Algebra With Inequalities — this is generally a bit tricky

The thing to remember here is that inequalities are just like regular equations:

$$5X < X + 2$$
$$5X = X + 2$$

in the sense that all the normal rules of algebra (See P.45) apply...

...**BUT WITH ONE BIG EXCEPTION**:

Whenever you MULTIPLY OR DIVIDE BY A NEGATIVE NUMBER, you must FLIP THE INEQUALITY SIGN.

Example: "Solve $5X < 6X + 2$"

ANS: First move the 6X over the "<" : $5X - 6X < 2$

combining the X-terms gives: $-X < 2$

To get rid of the "–" in front of X you need to divide both sides by –1 — but remember that means the "<" has to be flipped as well, which gives:

$X > -2$ i.e. *"X is greater than –2"* is the answer

(The < has flipped around into a >, because we divided by a –ve number)

This answer, $X > -2$, can be displayed as a shaded region on a number line like this:

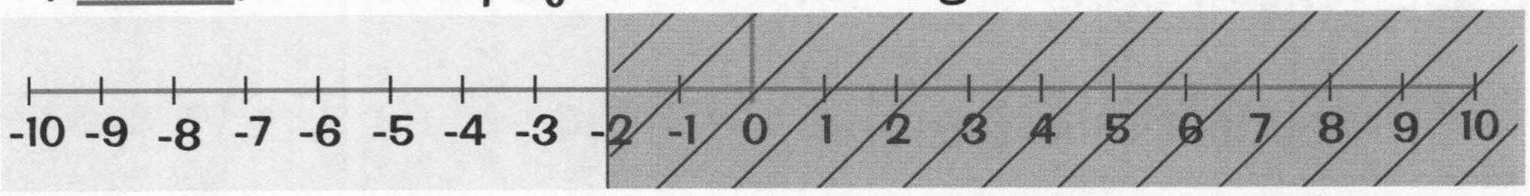

The main thing you should realise, is that MOST OF THE TIME you just treat the "<" or ">" as though it was an "=" and *do all the usual algebra* that you would for a regular equation. The "Big Exception" doesn't actually come up very often at all.

The Acid Test:

LEARN: The 4 Inequality Symbols, the similarity with EQUATIONS and the One Big Exception.

Now *turn over and write down what you've learned*.

1) Solve this inequality: $4X + 3 \leqslant 6X + 7$.

2) Find all the integer values of X which satisfy both $2X + 9 \geqslant 1$ and $4X < 6 + X$

Graphical Inequalities

This is easy so long as you remember the easy method for drawing graphs — i.e. a table of 3 values (see P.63).

The questions always involve SHADING A REGION ON A GRAPH, which is actually easy but it's always presented as some really horrid-looking algebra that puts most people right off before they even start.

The thing is, once you realise that the horrid-looking algebra just means something really simple then the whole thing becomes quite mind-numbingly simple. (!)

Method

1) **CONVERT each INEQUALITY to an EQUATION**
by simply putting an "=" in place of the "<"

2) **DO A TABLE OF 3 VALUES FOR EACH EQUATION**
and then draw the lines on the graph.

3) **SHADE THE ENCLOSED REGION**
The lines you've drawn will always enclose the region that you're after — and they nearly always ask you to shade it.

Example

"Shade the region represented by : $y < x + 2$, $x + y < 5$ and $y > 0$ "

(See what I mean about the horrid-looking algebra)

ANSWER:

1) CONVERT EACH INEQUALITY TO AN *EQUATION*:

$y < x + 2$ becomes $y = x + 2$,
$x + y < 5$ becomes $x + y = 5$,
$y > 0$ becomes $y = 0$

2) DO A TABLE OF 3 VALUES for each equation, and draw the lines on a graph.
e.g. for $y = x + 2$:

X	0	2	4
Y	2	4	6

3) SHADE THE ENCLOSED REGION, and Bob's your Uncle, it's done.

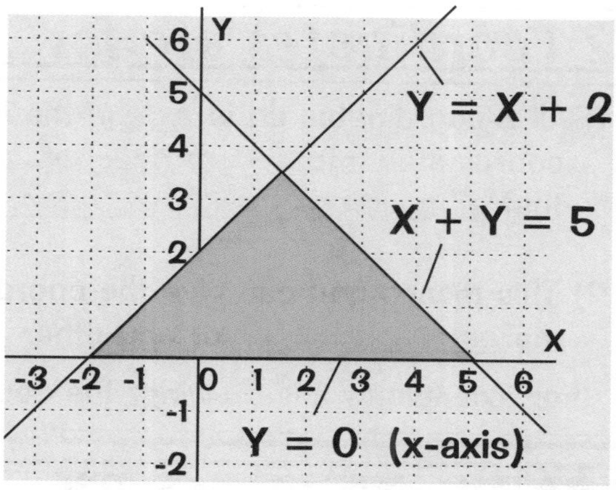

The Acid Test:

LEARN the Three Steps for doing graphical inequalities, then turn over and write them down.

1) Show on a graph the region enclosed by the following three conditions:

$X + Y < 6$, $Y > 0.5$, $Y < 2X - 2$

X, Y and Z Coordinates

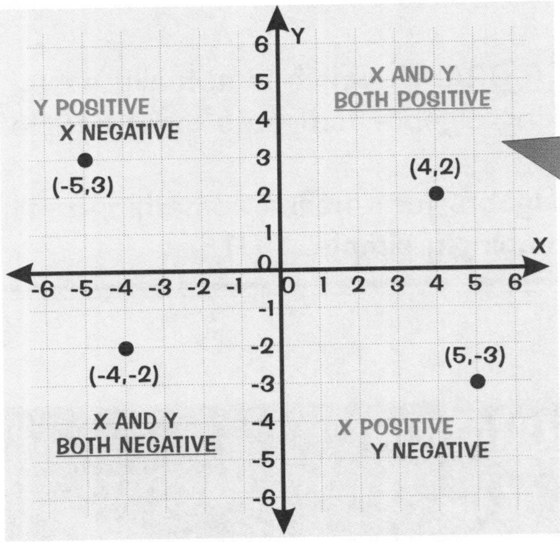

A graph has four different regions where the X- and Y- coordinates are either positive or negative.

This is the easiest region by far because here ALL THE COORDINATES ARE POSITIVE.

You have to be *dead careful* in the *OTHER REGIONS* though, because the X- and Y- coordinates could be negative, and that always makes life much more difficult.

X, Y Coordinates — getting them in the right order

You must always give COORDINATES in brackets like this: (x,y)

(x , y)

And you always have to be real careful to get them *the right way round*, X first, then Y. Here are *THREE POINTS* to help you remember:

1) The two coordinates are always in ALPHABETICAL ORDER, X then Y.
2) X is always the flat axis going ACROSS the page.
   In other words " X is a..cross " Get it! — x is a "×". (Hilarious isn't it)
3) Remember it's always IN THE HOUSE (→) and then UP THE STAIRS (↑),
   so it's ALONG first and then UP, i.e. X-coordinate first, and then Y-coordinate.

Z Coordinates are for 3-D space

1) All z-coordinates do is *extend* the normal x-y coordinates into a *third direction*, z, so that *all positions then have 3 coordinates:* *(x,y,z)*

2) This means you can give the coordinates of the *corners of a box* or any other 3-D SHAPE.

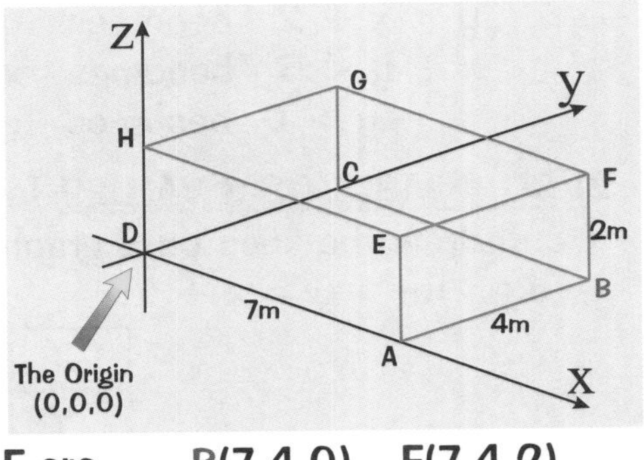

For example in this drawing, the coordinates of B and F are B(7,4,0) F(7,4,2)

The Acid Test:

OH — AND DON'T FORGET:
3 COORDINATES = 3-D SPACE
2 COORDINATES = 2-D SPACE

LEARN the 3 Rules for getting X and Y the right way round.
Then turn over and write it all down.

1) Write down the coordinates of the letters A to H on this graph:

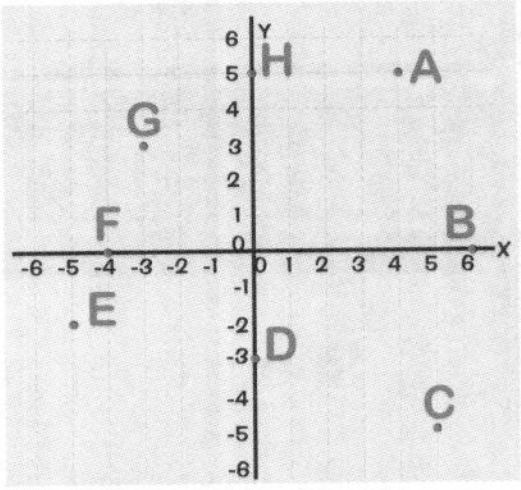

Easy Graphs You Should Know

If you want to make life easy for yourself, then you *definitely* need to know a few simple graphs straight off *without even having to blink*. These are they:

1) "X = a"

VERTICAL Lines

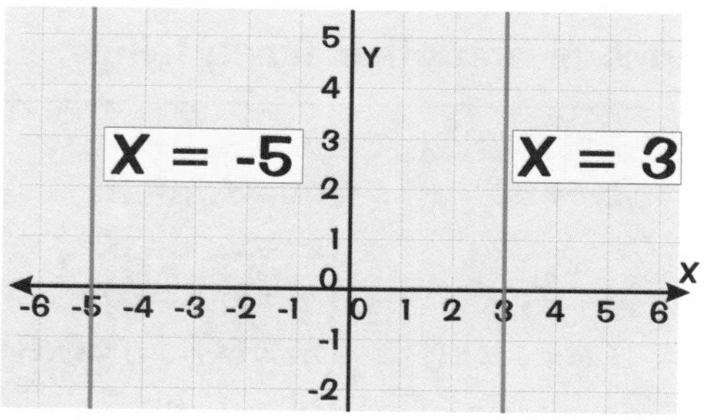

"X = a number" is a line that goes straight up through that number on the X-axis, e.g. X = 3 goes straight up through 3 on the X-axis as shown.

Don't forget: the y-axis is also the line "x = 0"

2) "Y = a"

HORIZONTAL Lines

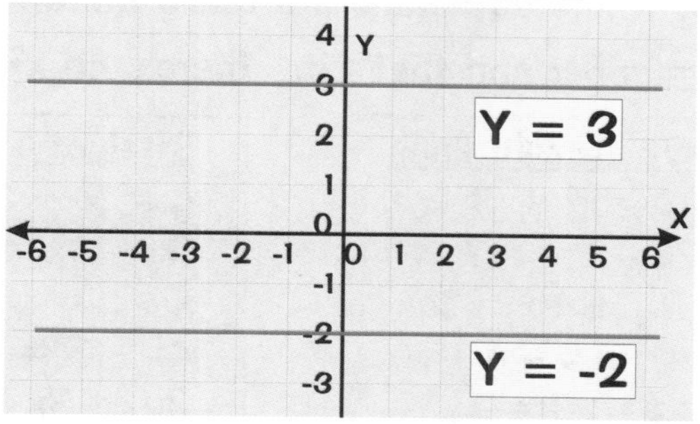

"Y = a number" is a line that goes straight across through that number on the Y-axis, e.g. Y = -2 goes straight through -2 on the Y-axis as shown.

Don't forget: the x-axis is also the line "y = 0"

3) "Y = X" and "Y = –X"

(The Main Diagonals)

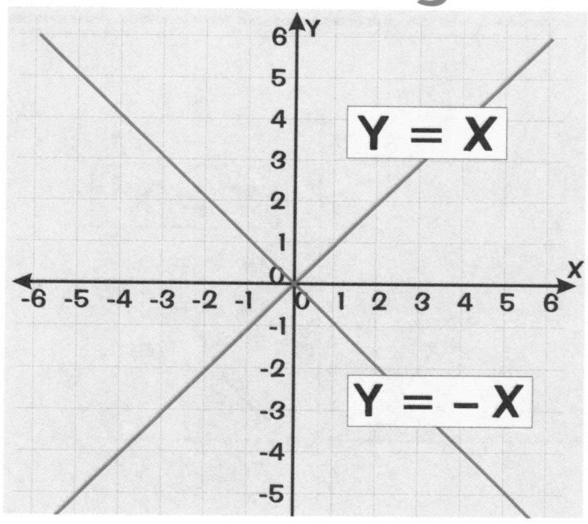

"Y = X" is the main diagonal that goes UPHILL from left to right.

"Y = -X" is the main diagonal that goes DOWNHILL from left to right.

4) "Y = AX" and "Y = –AX"

(Other Sloping Lines)

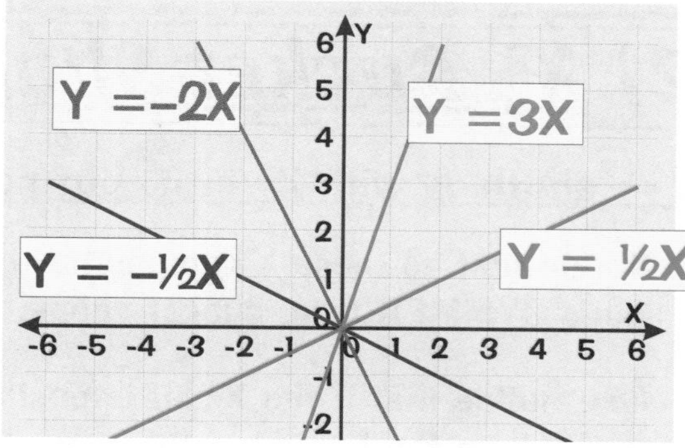

Y = AX and Y = -AX are the equations for A SLOPING LINE THROUGH THE ORIGIN.

The value of A is the *GRADIENT* of the line, so the BIGGER the number the STEEPER the slope, and a MINUS SIGN tells you it slopes DOWNHILL as shown by the ones above.

The Acid Test:

LEARN the FOUR EASY TYPES OF GRAPH, then turn over and WRITE IT ALL DOWN with examples.

Then *cover the page* and do these:

1) Write down the equations of *the four graphs shown here:*
2) Draw these 6 graphs: X = 3, Y = -4, Y = X, Y = -X, Y = 0, Y = -½X.

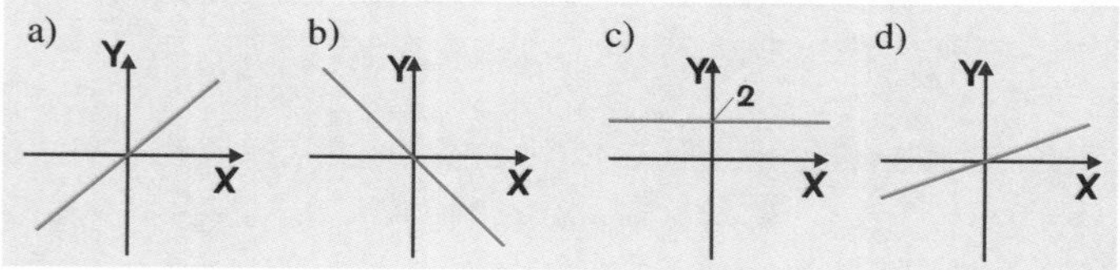

Four Graphs You Should Recognise

There are four types of graph that you should know the basic shape of just from looking at their equations — it really isn't as difficult as it sounds.

1) Straight Line Graphs: "Y = mx + c"

Straight line equations are really quite easy to spot — they have an x-term, a y-term and a number and that's it. There's no x^2 or x^3 or $1/x$ terms or any other fancy things.

NOT straight lines
$y = x^3 + 3$
$2y - 1/x = 7$
$1/y + 1/x = 2$
$x^2 = 4 - y$
$xy + 3 = 0$

Straight lines		Rearranged into "y = mx + c"	
$y = 2 + 3x$	→	$y = 3x + 2$	(m=3, c=2)
$2y - 4x = 7$	→	$y = 2x + 3\frac{1}{2}$	(m=2, c=3½)
$x - y = 0$	→	$y = x + 0$	(m=1, c=0)
$4x - 3 = 5y$	→	$y = 0.8x - 0.6$	(m=0.8, c=0.6)
$3y + 3x = 12$	→	$y = -x + 4$	(m=-1, c=4)

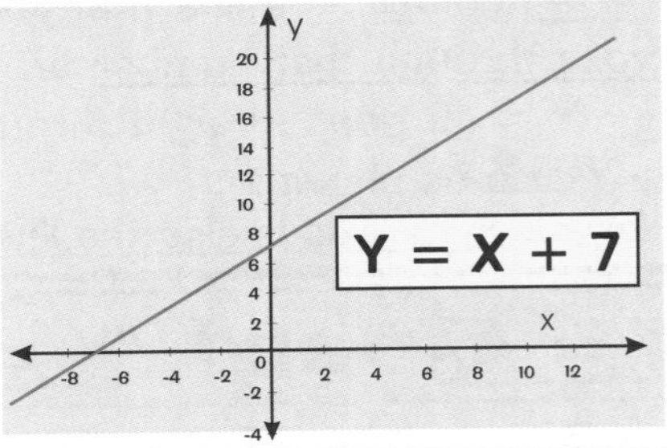

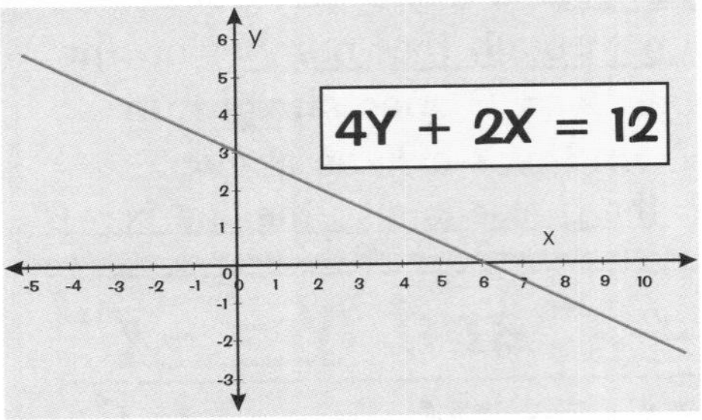

2) X^2 Bucket Shapes:

Y = anything with X^2 in it, but not X^3

Notice that all these X^2 graphs have the same SYMMETRICAL bucket shape.

Also notice that if the X^2 bit is positive (i.e. $+X^2$) then the bucket is the normal way up, but if the X^2 bit has a "minus" in front of it (i.e. $-X^2$) then the bucket is upside down.

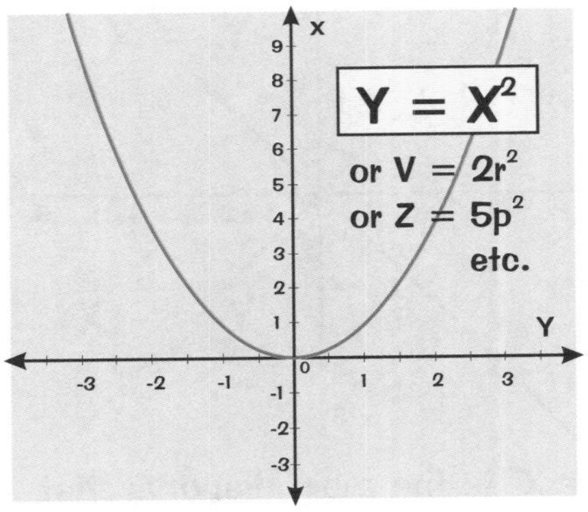

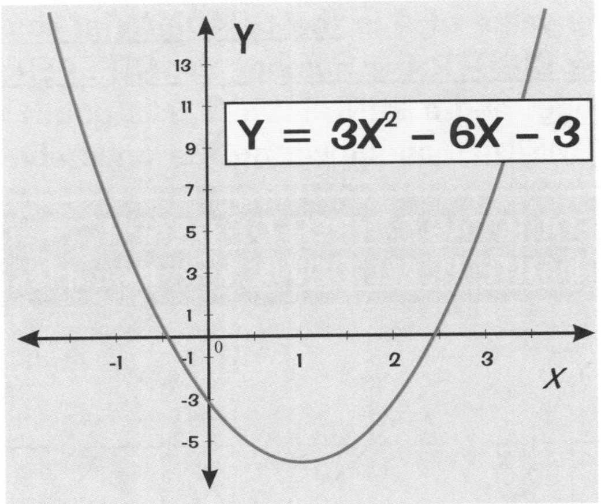

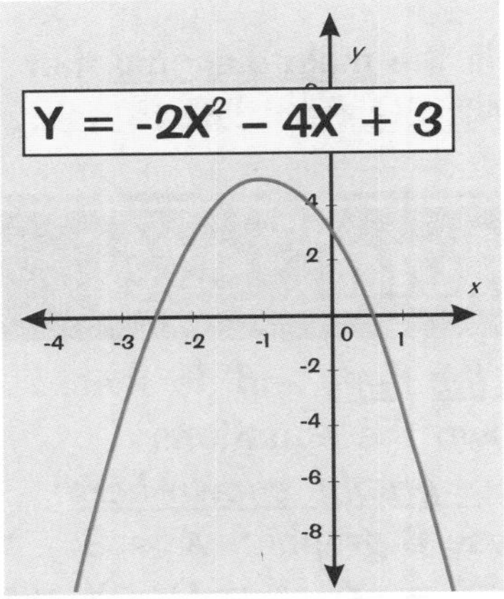

Four Graphs You Should Recognise

3) X^3 Graphs:

Y = "something with X^3 in it"

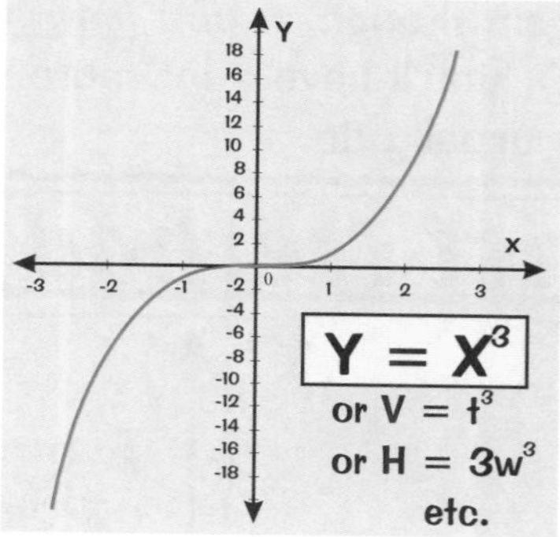

All X^3 graphs have the same basic *wiggle* in the middle, but it can be a flat wiggle or a more pronounced wiggle.

Notice that "$-X^3$ graphs" always come *down from top left* whereas the $+X^3$ ones go *up from bottom left*.

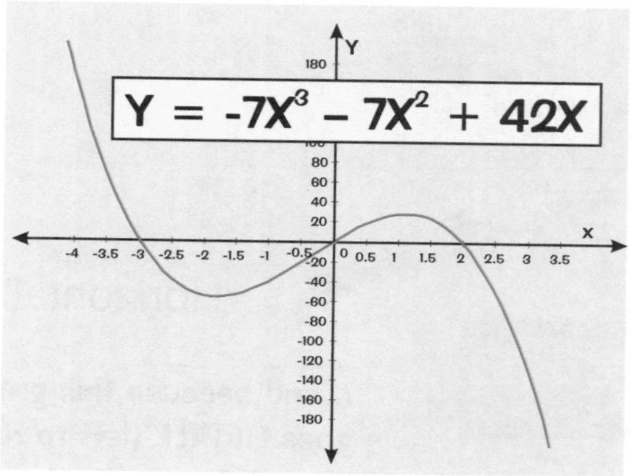

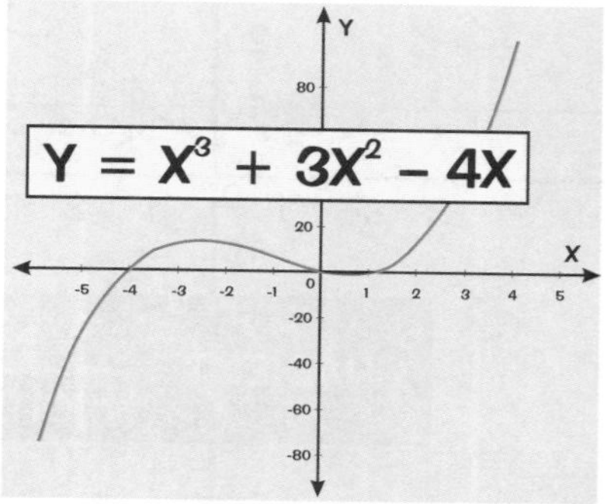

4) 1/X Graphs:

$Y = A/X$, where A is some number.

These graphs are all EXACTLY the same shape, the only difference being how close in they get at the corner. They are all *symmetrical about the line y=x*. This is also the graph you get when x and y are in *inverse proportion*.

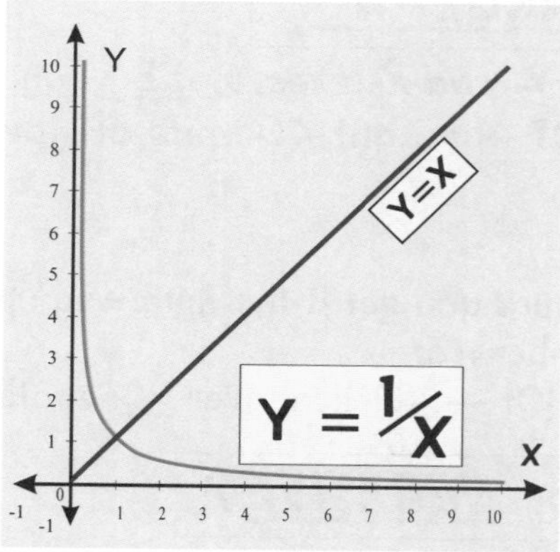

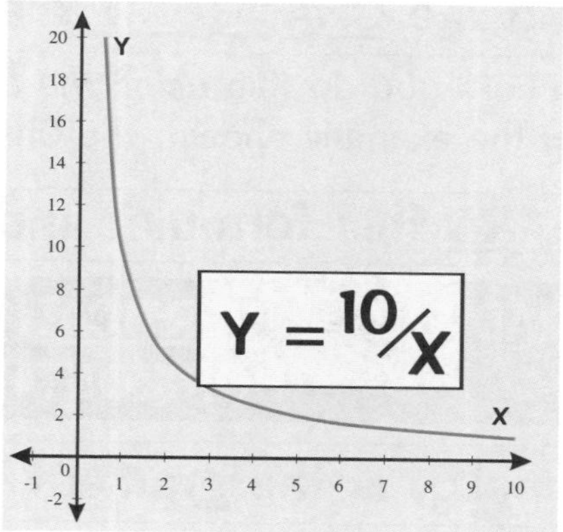

The Acid Test:

LEARN all the details about the 4 Types of Graph, their equations and their shapes.

Then *turn over* and *sketch three examples* of each of the *four types* of graph — and if you can also give some extra details about their equations, *so much the better*.
Remember, if you don't LEARN IT, then it's a waste of time even reading it. This is true for all revision.

Finding the Gradient of a Line

Working out the gradient of a straight line is a slightly involved business, and there are quite a few things that can go wrong.

Once again though, if you *learn and follow the steps below* and treat it as a STRICT METHOD, you'll have a lot more success than if you try and fudge your way through it, like you usually do.

Strict Method For Finding Gradient

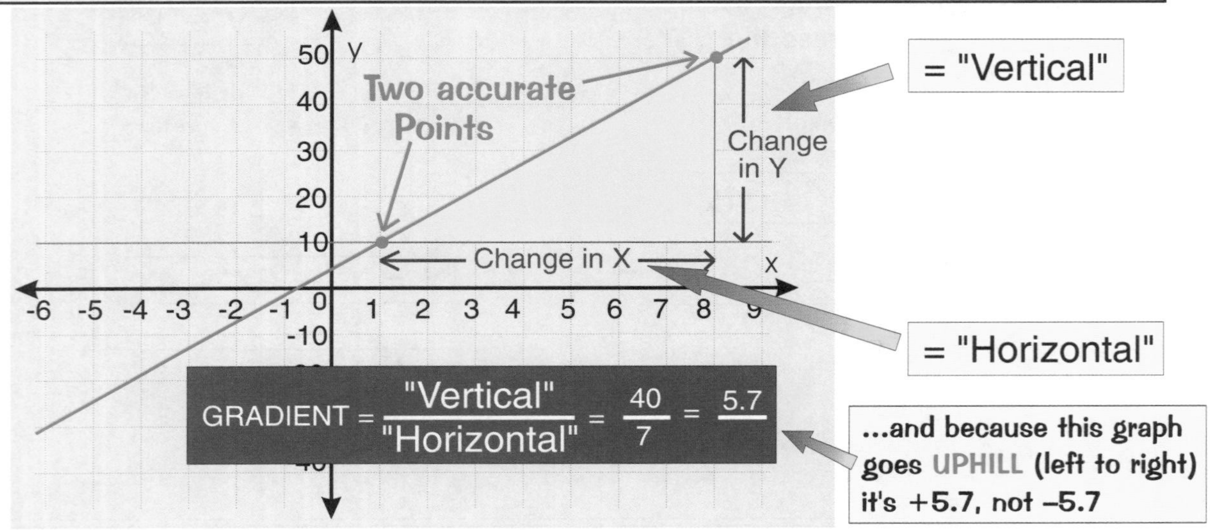

1) Find *TWO ACCURATE POINTS*, reasonably far apart

Both in the *upper right quadrant* if possible, (to keep all the numbers positive and so reduce the chance of errors).

2) *COMPLETE THE TRIANGLE* as shown

3) Find the CHANGE IN Y and the CHANGE IN X

Make sure you do this *using the SCALES on the Y- and X- axes*, not by counting cm! (So in the example shown, the Change in Y is NOT 4cm, but *40 units* off the Y-axis.)

4) *LEARN* this formula, and use it:

$$\text{GRADIENT} = \frac{\text{VERTICAL}}{\text{HORIZONTAL}}$$

Make sure you get it the right way up too! Remember it's: VERy HOt — VERtical over HOrizontal

5) Finally, is the gradient *POSITIVE* or *NEGATIVE*?

If it slopes UPHILL left → right (↗) then it's +ve

If it slopes DOWNHILL left → right (↘) then it's –ve (so put a minus(–) in front of it)

The Acid Test:

LEARN the FIVE STEPS for finding a gradient then turn over and WRITE THEM DOWN from memory.

1) Plot these 3 points on a graph: (0,3) (2,0) (5,-4.5) and then join them up with a straight line. Now carefully apply the FIVE STEPS to find the gradient of the line.

Plotting Straight Line Graphs

Some people wouldn't know a straight line equation if it ran up and bit them, but they're pretty easy to spot really — they just have two letters and a few numbers, but nothing fancy like squared or cubed.

Anyway, in the Exam you'll be expected to be able to draw the graphs of straight line equations. "y = mx + c" is the hard way of doing it, but here's TWO NICE EASY WAYS of doing it:

1) The "Table of 3 Values" Method

You can EASILY draw the graph of ANY EQUATION using this EASY method:

1) Choose 3 VALUES OF X and draw up a wee table,
2) WORK OUT THE Y-VALUES,
3) PLOT THE COORDINATES, and DRAW THE LINE.

If it's a *straight line equation*, the 3 points will be in a *dead straight line* with each other, which is the usual check you do when you've drawn it — if they aren't, then it could be a curve and you'll need to do *more values in your table* to find out what on earth's going on.

Example:

"Draw the graph of Y = 2X – 3"

1) DRAW UP A TABLE with some *suitable values* of X. Choosing X = 0, 2, 4 is usually cool enough. i.e.

X	0	2	4
Y			

2) FIND THE Y-VALUES by putting each X-value into the equation:

X	0	2	4
Y	-3	1	5

(e.g. When X = 4, $y = 2X - 3 \;=\; 2\times4 - 3 = 5$ *)*

3) PLOT THE POINTS and DRAW THE LINE.

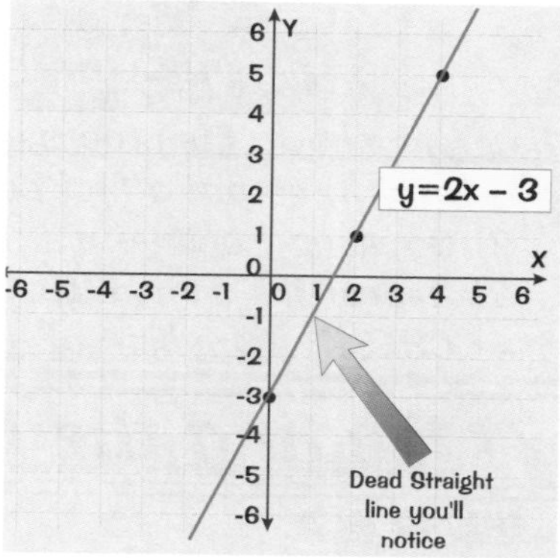

2) The "X = 0", "Y = 0" Method

This is especially good for typical linear programming equations of the form: "ax + by = c"

1) Set x=0 in the equation, and FIND Y — this is where it CROSSES THE Y-AXIS.
2) Set y=0 in the equation and FIND X — this is where it CROSSES THE X-AXIS.
3) Plot these two points and join them up with a straight line — *and just hope it should be a straight line, since with only 2 points you can't really tell, can you!*

Example:

"Draw the graph of 5x + 3y = 15"

1) Putting x = 0 gives "3y = 15" ⇒ y = 5
2) Putting y = 0 gives "5x = 15" ⇒ x = 3
3) So plot y = 5 on the y-axis and x = 3 on the x-axis and join them up with a straight line:

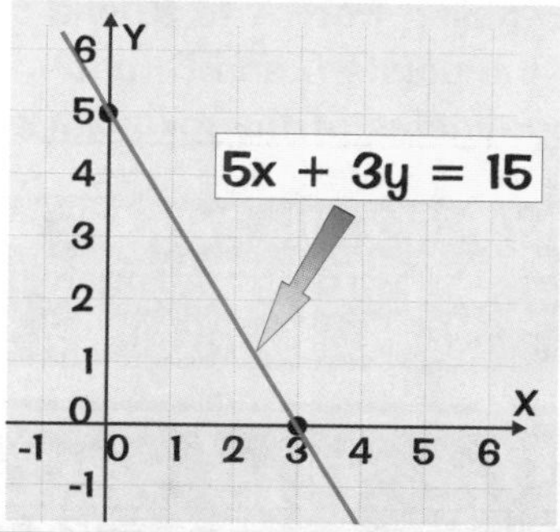

Only doing 2 points is risky unless you're sure the equation is definitely a straight line — but then that's the big thrill of living life on the edge, isn't it.

The Acid Test:

LEARN the details of these TWO EASY METHODS then turn over and write down all you know.

1) Draw these graphs using both methods a) y = 4 + x b) 4y + 3x = 12 c) y = 6 – 2x

Straight Line Graphs

Using y = mx + c

$y = mx + c$ is the general equation for a straight line graph, and you need to remember:

"m" is equal to the GRADIENT of the graph

"c" is the value WHERE IT CROSSES THE Y-AXIS and is called the INTERCEPT.

1) Drawing a Straight Line using "y = mx + c"

The main thing is being able to identify "m" and "c" and knowing what to do with them:
BUT WATCH OUT — people often mix up "m" and "c", especially with say, "$y = 5 + 2x$"
REMEMBER: "m" is the number IN FRONT OF X and "c" is the number ON ITS OWN.

Method

1) Get the equation into the form "$y = mx + c$".
2) IDENTIFY "m" and "c" CAREFULLY.
3) PUT A DOT ON THE Y-AXIS at the value of c.
4) Then go ALONG ONE UNIT and up or down by the value of m and make another dot.
5) Repeat the same "step" in both directions as shown:
6) Finally CHECK that the gradient LOOKS RIGHT.

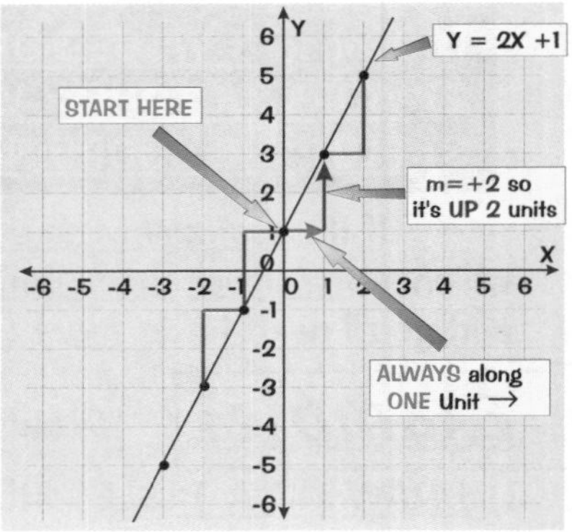

The graph shows the process for the equation "$y = 2x + 1$":

1) "c" = 1, so put a first dot at y = 1 on the y-axis.
2) Go along 1 unit → and then up by 2 because "m" = +2.
3) Repeat the same step, 1→ 2↑ in both directions. (i.e. 1 ← 2 ↓ the other way)
4) CHECK: a gradient of +2 should be quite steep and uphill left to right — which it is.

2) Finding the Equation Of a Straight Line Graph

THIS IS EASY:
1) Find where the graph CROSSES THE Y-AXIS.
   This is the value of "c".
2) Find the value of the GRADIENT (see P.62).
   This is the value of "m"
3) Now just put these values for "m" and "c" into "$y = mx + c$"
   ~ and there you have it!

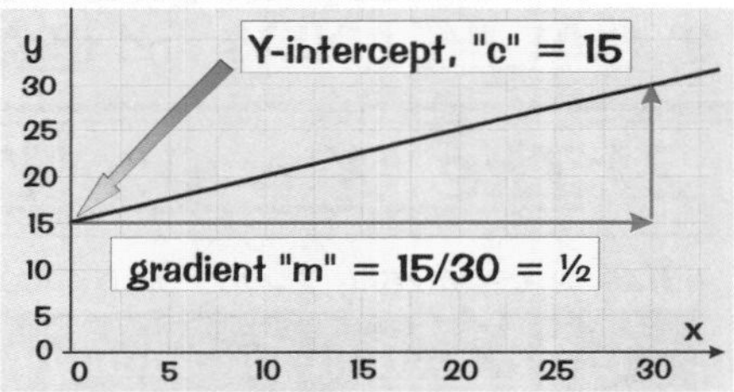

For the graph shown here, m=½ and c = 15 so "$y = mx + c$" becomes "$y = ½x + 15$"

3) Finding the Coordinates of the Midpoint

This is really easy — if you've got a line (or part-line) stretching from A to B, and you know the coordinates of the points A and B, you can easily work out the coordinates of the midpoint along that line.

JUST TAKE THE AVERAGE OF THE X-COORDINATES AND THE AVERAGE OF THE Y-COORDINATES AND PLONK THEM IN A PAIR OF BRACKETS.

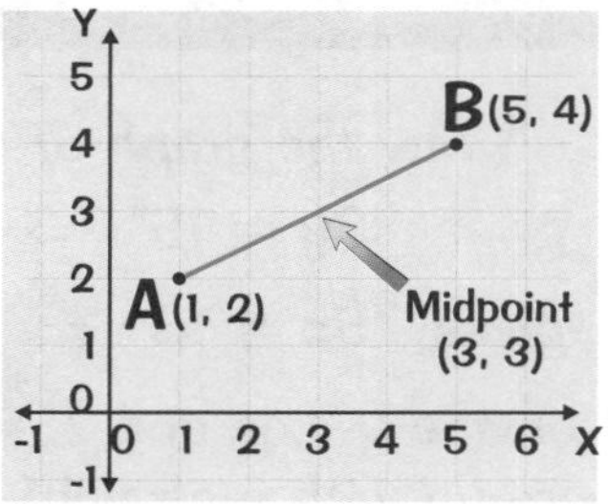

A = (1, 2) ⇒ X=1, Y=2
B = (5, 4) ⇒ X=5, Y=4
Average of X-coordinates = (1 + 5) ÷ 2 = 3
Average of Y-coordinates = (2 + 4) ÷ 2 = 3
PLONK 'EM TOGETHER...
Average coordinates = coordinates of midpoint = (3, 3)

The Acid Test:

LEARN THE DETAILS of the two methods for "$y = mx + c$".
Then TURN OVER and WRITE IT ALL DOWN.

1) Using "$y = mx + c$" draw the graphs of $y=x - 3$ and $y=4 - 2x$.
2) Using "$y = mx + c$" find the equations of these 3 graphs →
3) Give the coordinates of the midpoint, N, of the line segment from L(16, 12) to M(4, 3).

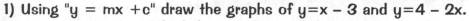

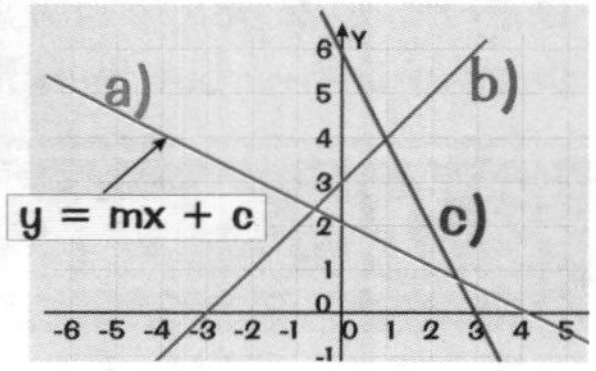

Travel Graphs

A nice easy page for you, to help relieve the stress of the extremely grisly Module Five.

Travel Graphs — Always the same and always Easy

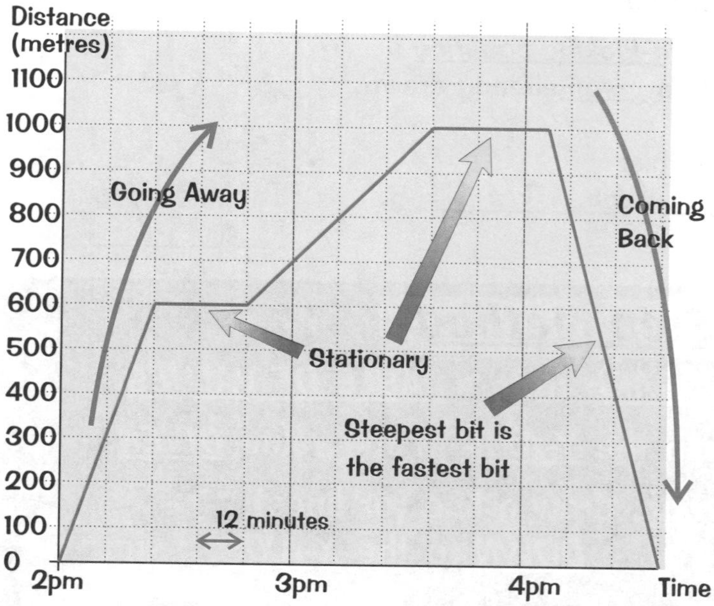

1) Make sure you know *all these details* about travel graphs.

2) Also, always make sure you know exactly *how much time* each interval on the Time axis actually is. On this graph there are *5 divisions* for each *hour*, so each one must be *12 minutes* (60÷5).

THE SIX KEY POINTS ABOUT TRAVEL GRAPHS

1) A TRAVEL GRAPH is always DISTANCE (↑) against TIME (→).
2) For any section, SLOPE (gradient) = SPEED, but watch out for the UNITS.
3) FLAT SECTIONS are where it's STOPPED.
4) The STEEPER the graph the FASTER it's going.
5) UPHILL SECTIONS mean it's TRAVELLING AWAY from its starting point.
6) DOWNHILL SECTIONS means it's COMING BACK towards its starting point.

A Typical Tricky Question:

"What's the speed of the return section on the graph shown above?"

ANSWER Speed = gradient
= 1000m / 30mins = 33.33 m/min (metres per minute)
or 1km ÷ ½hr = 2 km/h (kilometres per hour)
or 1000m ÷ 1800s = 0.56 m/s (metres per second)

Note that the answer (and its units) depends very much on what units you use to work it out.

The Acid Test:

LEARN all the details on the graph above and then the Six Key Points for Travel Graphs.

Now cover the page and write down everything you've learnt.

1) For the travel graph above, work out the speed of the middle section, in km/h.
2) Also, describe the whole sequence of events between 2pm and 4:36pm.

Solving Equations Using Graphs

In your Exam you might get a question asking you to solve an equation using a graph. These aren't too bad, so long as you know how to tackle them. Learn all this stuff:

The Answers are where The Y-value Hits the Graph

The typical question will have a nasty-looking equation a bit like this: $y = x^3 + 2x^2 + 4$ and a graph already drawn (or mostly done for you anyway).
Then they'll ask you something like this:
"From the graph, find the value of x which makes $y = 8$."
This is how you do it:

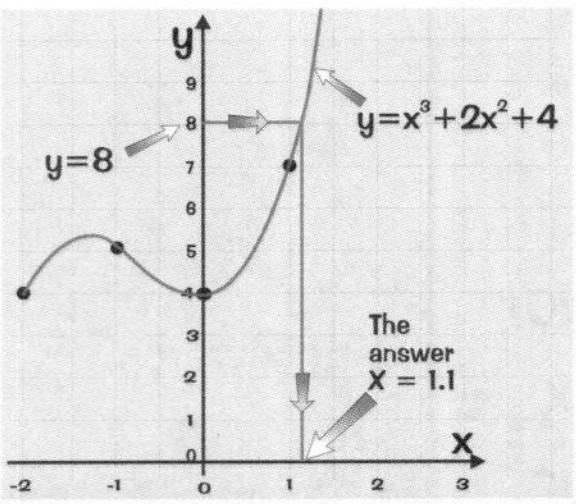

The Easy Peasy Four-Step Method

1) Draw (or finish off) the GRAPH from a TABLE OF VALUES.
2) Draw a line ACROSS from the Y-AXIS at the value GIVEN.
3) Where it crosses the graph, draw a line (or lines) DOWN to the X-AXIS.
4) READ OFF the X-VALUES — they're the ANSWERS.

Example

"Complete the table of values shown for the equation $y = 25x - 5x^2$.
Plot the points and draw the graph.
Use the graph to find the values of x when $y = 25$."

X	0	1	2	3	4	5
Y		20				0

Answer

X	0	1	2	3	4	5
Y	0	20	30	30	20	0

1) Complete the table of values and draw the graph.
   Note the nice smooth curve and the curved peak.
   DON'T EVER join the two points near the peak with a ridiculous straight line.

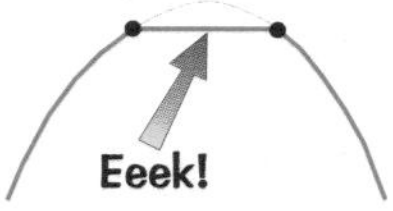

2) Draw a line ACROSS from the Y-axis (using the given y-value of 25).
3) Where it HITS THE CURVE, go DOWN to the X-axis.
4) Read off the X-values. It's as easy as that.

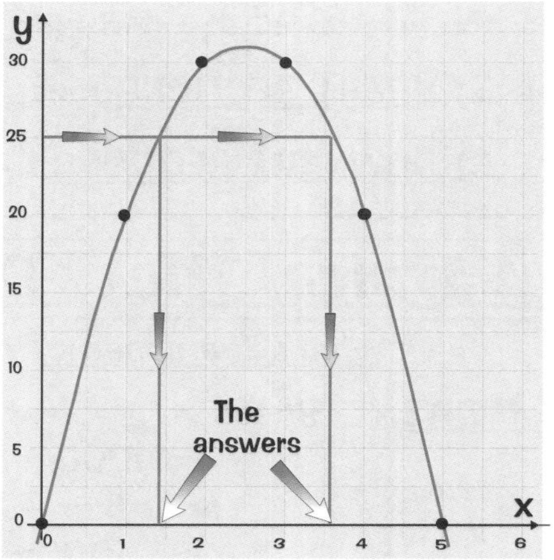

So from the graph we get the ANSWERS to be X = 1.4 or X = 3.6.

The Acid Test:

LEARN the first big coloured heading, the Four Step Method and all the details on both graphs.

Cover the page and write down everything you've learnt.
1) Using the above graph for $y = 25x - 5x^2$, find the values of x which give $y = 15$.
2) Do a table of values and a graph for $y = 2x^3 - 3x$. Find the value of x when $y = 12$.

Typical Graph Questions

There's a lot of fiddly details involved in graph questions: getting the right values in the table; plotting the right points; and getting the final answers from your graph.
If you want to get all these easy marks, then you've got to learn all these little tricks:

Filling in The Table of Values

A typical question: *"Complete the table of values for the equation $y = x^2 - 4x + 3$"*

x	-2	-1	0	1	2	3	4	5	6
y				0			3		15

WHAT YOU DON'T DO is try to punch it all into the calculator in one go. Not good. The rest of the question hinges on this table of values and one silly mistake here could cost you a lot of marks. This might look like a long-winded method but it takes far less time than you think and is the only REALLY SAFE method.

1) For EVERY value in the table you should WRITE THIS OUT:

For x=4: $y = x^2 - 4x + 3$
$= 4^2 - 4\times4 + 3$
$= 16 - 16 + 3$
$= 3$

For x=-1: $y = x^2 - 4x + 3$
$= (-1\times-1) - (4\times-1) + 3$
$= 1 - -4 + 3 = 1 + 4 + 3$
$= 8$

2) Make sure you can reproduce the y-values they've already given you...

... BEFORE you fill in the spaces in the table. This is really important to make sure you're doing it right, before you start cheerfully working out a pile of wrong values!

I wouldn't tell you all this without good reason, so ignore it at your peril.

Plotting the Points and Drawing the Curve

Here again there are easy marks to be won and lost — this all matters:

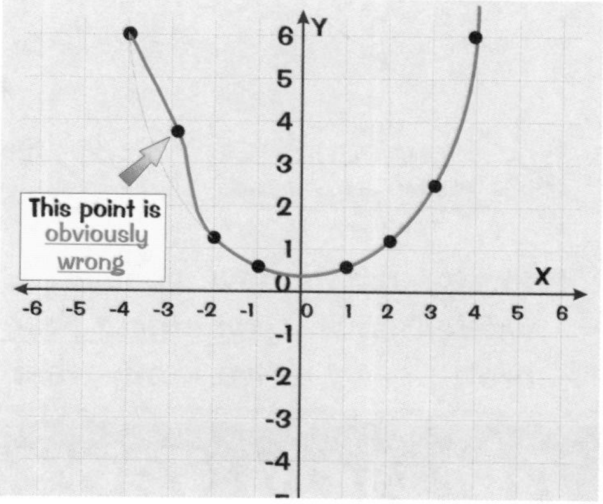

1) GET THE AXES THE RIGHT WAY ROUND: The values from the FIRST row or column are ALWAYS plotted *on the X-axis*.
2) PLOT THE POINTS CAREFULLY, and don't mix up the x and y values.
3) The points will ALWAYS form a DEAD STRAIGHT LINE or a COMPLETELY SMOOTH CURVE. If they don't, they're *wrong*.
4) A graph from an ALGEBRA EQUATION, must always be drawn as a SMOOTH CURVE (or a dead straight line). You only use lots of short straight line sections to join points in *"Data Handling"* when it's called a "frequency polygon". (See P.5)

NEVER EVER *let one point drag your line off* in some ridiculous direction — if one point seems out of place, *check the value in the table* and then check the position where you've plotted it. When a graph is generated from an equation, *you never get spikes or lumps* — only MISTAKES.

Typical Graph Questions

Getting Answers from Your Graph

1) FOR A SINGLE CURVE OR LINE, you ALWAYS get the answer by *drawing a straight line to the graph from one axis*, and then *down or across to the other axis*, as shown here:

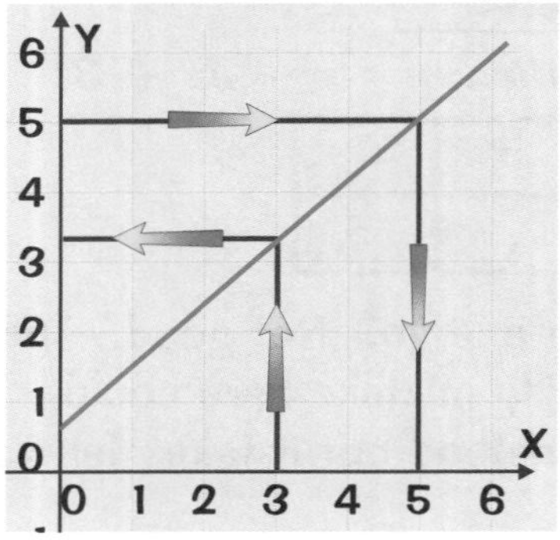

You should be *fully expecting* this to happen so that even if you don't understand the question, you can still have a pretty good stab at it:

If the question said *"Find the value of y when x is equal to 3"*, ALL YOU DO IS THIS: *start at 3 on the x-axis, go straight up to the graph, then straight over to the y-axis and read off the value, which in this case is y = 3.2* (as shown opposite).

2) IF TWO LINES CROSS.....
you can bet your very last fruitcake the answer to one of the questions will simply be:
THE VALUES OF X AND Y WHERE THEY CROSS
and you should be expecting that *before they even ask it.* (See Simultaneous Eqns. P.54).

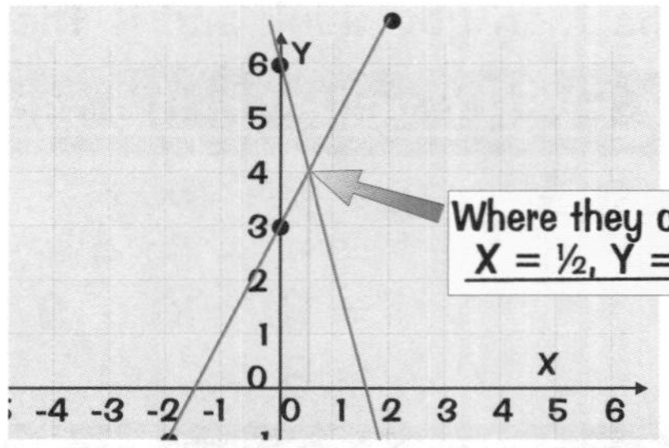

What The Gradient of a Graph MEANS

No matter what the graph, THE MEANING OF THE GRADIENT is always simply :

(Y-axis UNITS) PER (X-axis UNITS)

EXAMPLES:

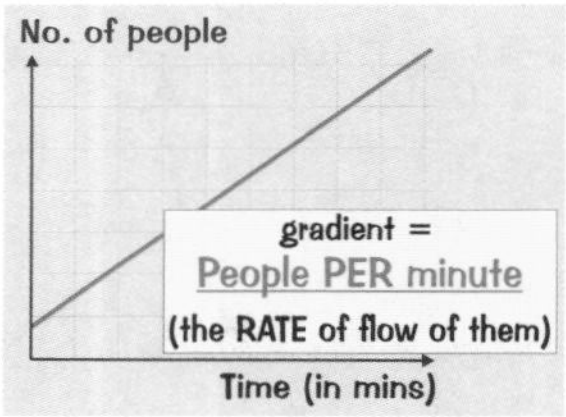

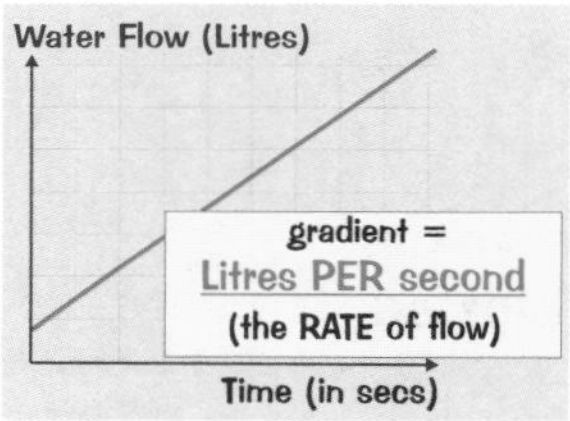

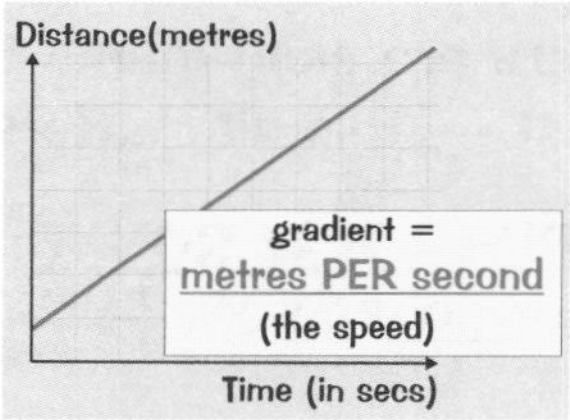

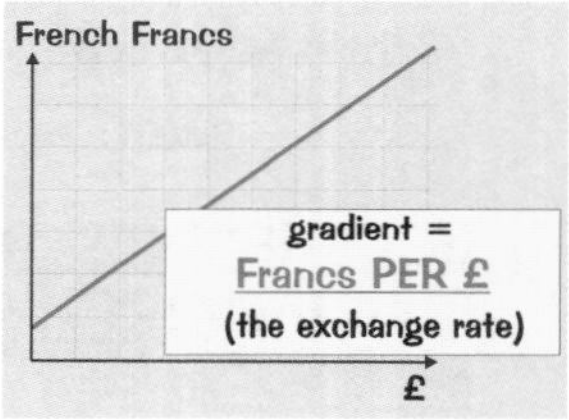

Some gradients have special names like *Exchange Rate* or *Speed*, but once you've written down *"something PER something"* using the Y-axis and X-axis UNITS, it's then pretty easy to work out what the gradient represents.

The Acid Test:

LEARN the 2 Rules for doing tables of values, the 4 points for drawing graphs, the 2 simple Rules for getting answers, and the meaning of gradient.

Now turn over and *write it all down from memory*. Then *try again until you can do it*.

1) *Complete the table of values* at the top of the previous page (using the proper methods!), and then *draw the graph* taking note of the Four Points.
2) From your graph find the value of y when x is 4.2, and the values of x when y=12.
3) If I drew a graph of "miles covered" up the y-axis and "gallons used" along the x-axis, and worked out the gradient, what would the value of it tell me?

The Four Transformations

T ranslation	—	ONE Detail
E nlargement	—	TWO Details
R otation	—	THREE Details
R eflection	—	ONE Detail
Y		

1) Use the name *TERRY* to remember the 4 types.
2) You must always specify *all the details* for each type.
3) It'll help if you remember which properties remain *unchanged* in each transformation, too.

1) TRANSLATION

You must Specify this ONE detail:

1) The VECTOR OF TRANSLATION $\begin{pmatrix} x \rightarrow \\ \uparrow y \end{pmatrix}$ (See P.85 on vector notation)

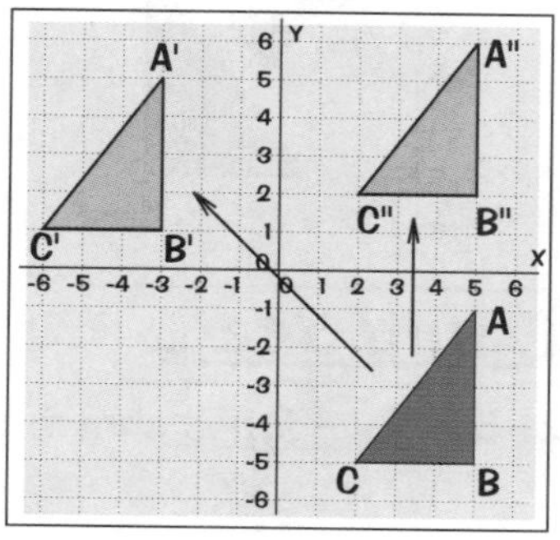

ABC to A'B'C' is a *translation of* $\begin{pmatrix} -8 \\ 6 \end{pmatrix}$

ABC to A"B"C" is a *translation of* $\begin{pmatrix} 0 \\ 7 \end{pmatrix}$

All that changes in a translation is the *POSITION* of the object — *everything else* remains *unchanged*.

2) ENLARGEMENT

You must Specify these 2 details:

1) The SCALE FACTOR
2) The CENTRE of Enlargement

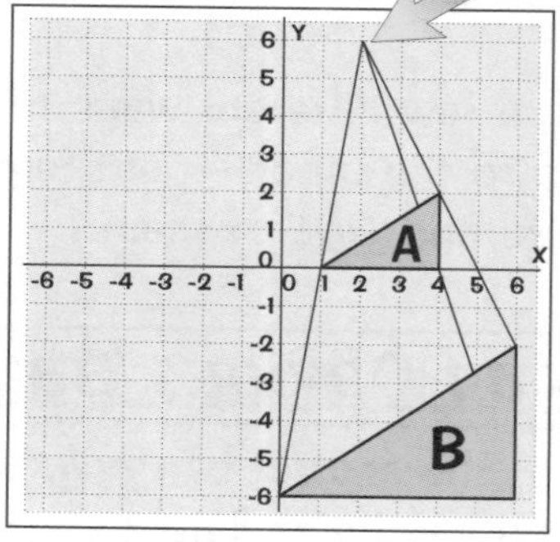

From A to B is an enlargement of scale factor 2, and centre (2,6).

From B to A is an enlargement of scale factor 1/2 and centre (2,6).

With enlargement, the *ANGLES* of the object, the *RATIOS* of the lengths of the sides, and the object's *ORIENTATION* remain *unchanged*. Everything else *can* change.

3) ROTATION

You must Specify these 3 details:

1) ANGLE turned
2) DIRECTION (Clockwise or..)
3) CENTRE of Rotation

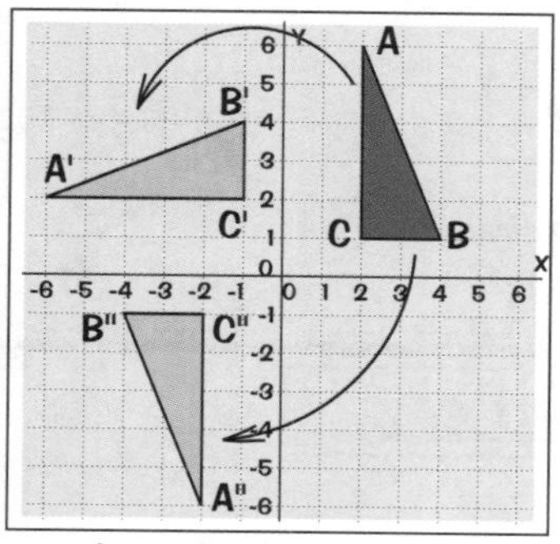

ABC to A'B'C' is a Rotation of 90°, anticlockwise, ABOUT the origin.

ABC to A"B"C" is a Rotation of half a turn (180°), clockwise, ABOUT the origin.

The only things that change in a rotation are the *POSITION* and the *ORIENTATION* of the object. *Everything else* remains *unchanged*.

4) REFLECTION

You must Specify this ONE detail:

1) The MIRROR LINE

A to B is a reflection IN the Y-axis.

A to C is a reflection IN the line Y=X

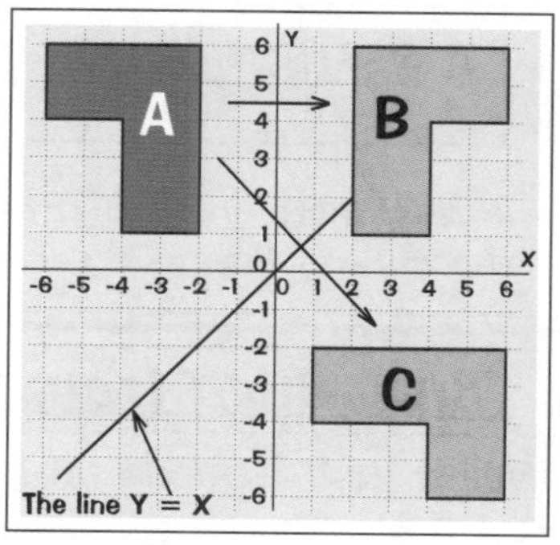

With reflection, the *POSITION* and *ORIENTATION* of the object are the *only things that change*.

The Acid Test:

LEARN the names of the Four Transformations and the details that go with each. When you think you know it, turn over and write it all down.

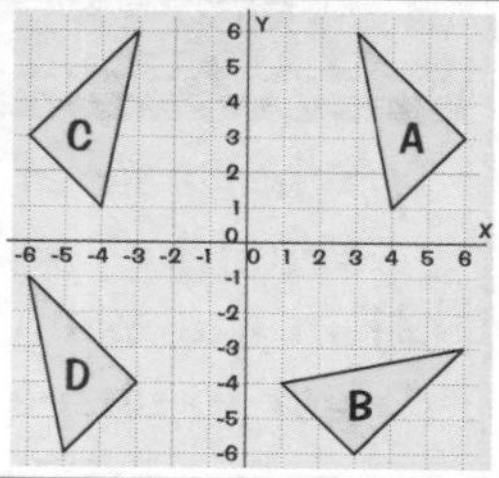

1) Describe *fully* these transformations: A — B, B — C, C — A, A — D.

Combinations of Transformations

In Exam questions they'll often do something *horrid* like *stick two transformations together* and then ask you what combination gets you from shape A to shape B. Be *ready*.

The Better You Know Them All — The Easier it is

These kinds of question aren't so bad — but *ONLY* if you've *LEARNT* the *four transformations* on the last page *really well* — if you don't know them, then you certainly won't do too well at spotting a *combination* of one followed by another.
That's because the method is basically *"Try it and see..."*

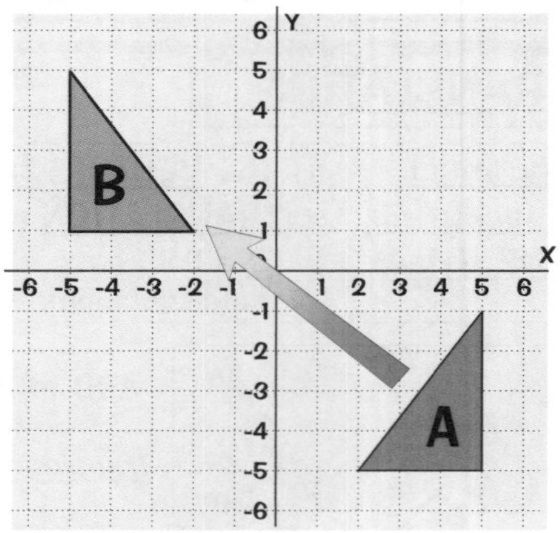

Example

"What combination of two transformations takes you from triangle A to triangle B?"

(There's usually a few different ways of getting from one shape to the other — but remember you only need to find *ONE* of them.)

Method: Try an Obvious Transformation First, and See...

If you *think* about it, the answer can *only* be a combination of two of the *four types* shown on the last page, so you can immediately start to *narrow it down*:

1) Since the shapes are the *same size* we can *rule out enlargements*.
2) Next, *try a reflection* (in either the X-axis or the Y-axis). Here we've tried a reflection in the *Y-axis*, to give shape A':
3) You should now easily be able to see the *final step* from A' to B — it's a *translation* of $\begin{pmatrix}0\\6\end{pmatrix}$.

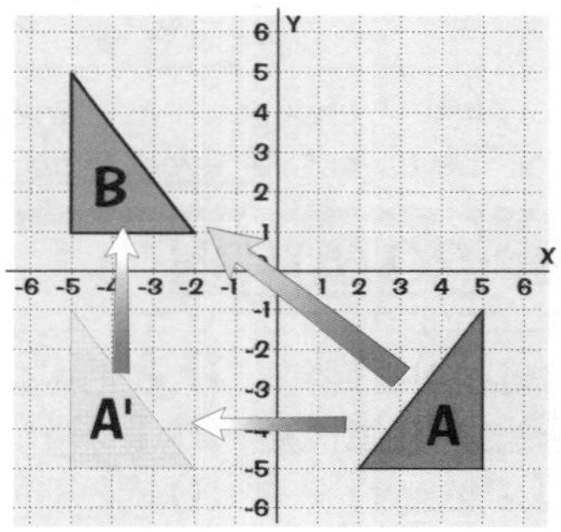

And that's it *DONE* — from A to B is simply a combination of:

A *REFLECTION IN THE Y-AXIS* followed by a *TRANSLATION OF* $\begin{pmatrix}0\\6\end{pmatrix}$

At least that's one answer anyway. If instead we decided to reflect it in the X-axis first (as shown here) then we'd get another answer (see Acid Test below) — but both are right.

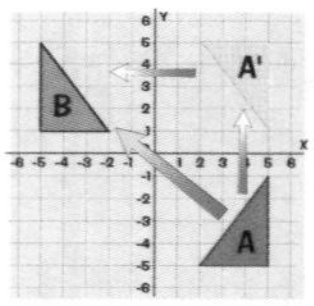

"But which transformation do I try first?" I hear you cry...

Well it just depends on *how it looks*.
But the *more transformation questions* you do, the more obvious that first guess becomes.
In other words: the more you *practise*, the *easier* you'll be able to do it — surprise surprise...

The Acid Test:

LEARN the *main points* on this page.
Then *cover it up* and *write them all down*.

1) What pair of transformations will convert shape C into shape D? What pair will convert shape D to shape C?
2) In the example above, find the other transformation needed to get to shape B after reflecting shape A in the X-axis.

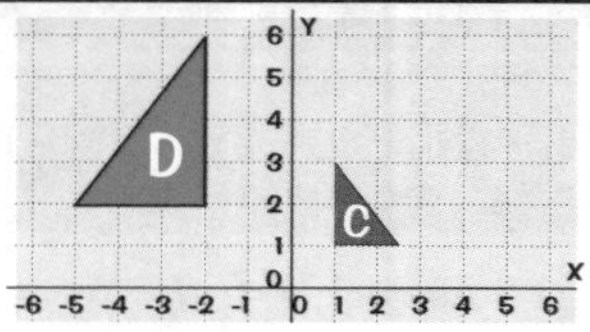

Enlargements — The 4 Key Features

1) If the Scale Factor is BIGGER THAN 1 then the shape gets BIGGER.

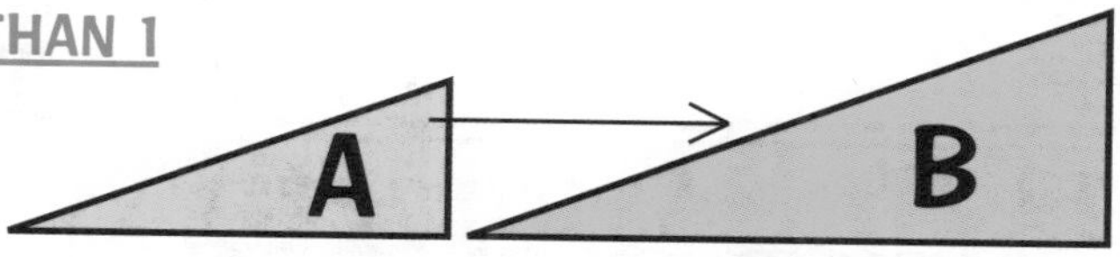

A to B is an Enlargement, Scale Factor 1½

2) If the Scale Factor is SMALLER than 1 (i.e. a fraction like ½), then the shape gets SMALLER.

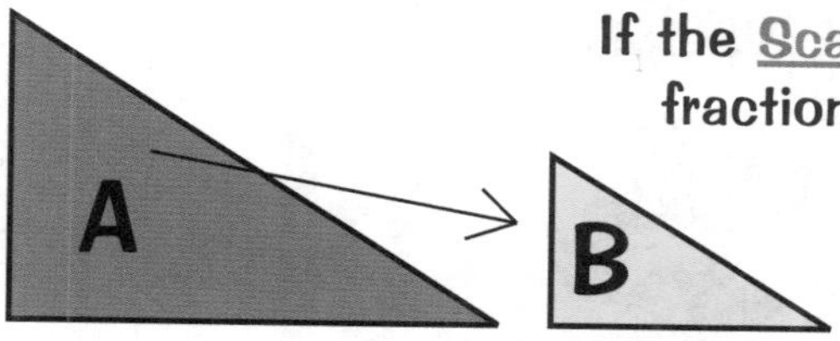

A to B is an Enlargement of Scale Factor ½

(Really this is a *reduction*, but you still call it an Enlargement, Scale Factor ½)

3) Enlargement Scale Factor 3

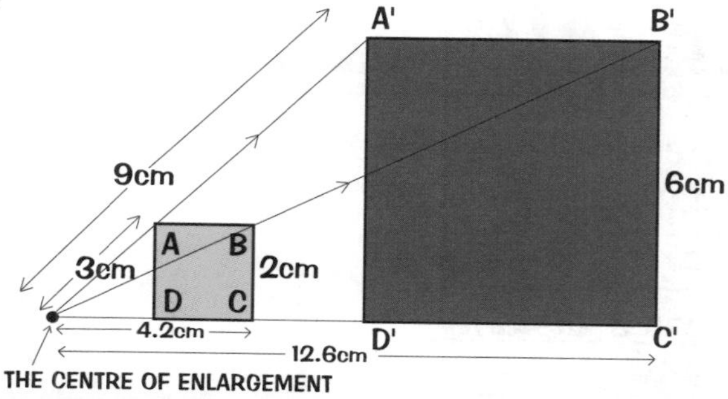

The Scale Factor also tells you the RELATIVE DISTANCE of old points and new points from the Centre of Enlargement.

This is VERY USEFUL FOR DRAWING AN ENLARGEMENT, because you can use it to trace out the positions of the new points from the centre of enlargement, as shown in the diagram.

4) The lengths of the big and small shapes are related to the Scale Factor by this VERY important Formula Triangle WHICH YOU MUST LEARN:

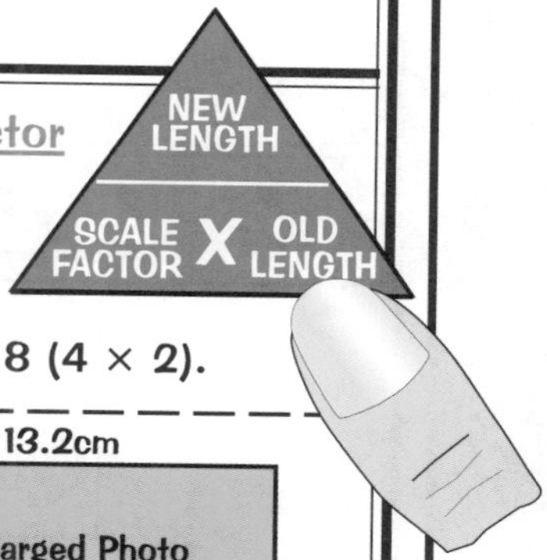

Obviously, if the length of a single side is multiplied by the scale factor, then the perimeter will also change by the same amount — e.g. a square of side-length 1 enlarged by scale factor 2 will have sides of length 2 and a perimeter changed from 4 to 8 (4 × 2).

This now lets you to tackle the classic "Enlarged photo" Exam question with breathtaking triviality:

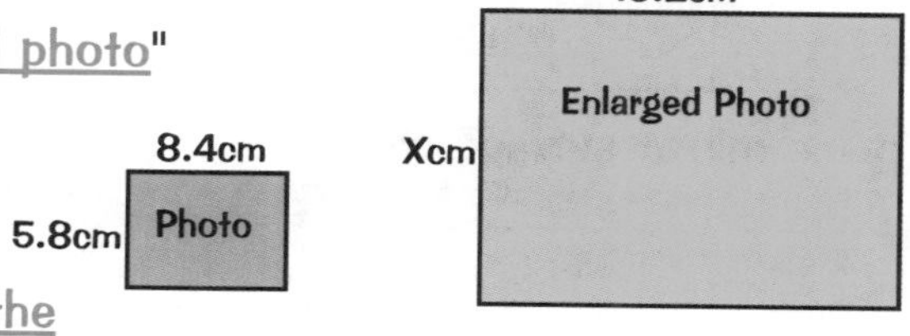

To find the width of the enlarged photo we use the formula triangle TWICE, (firstly to find the Scale Factor, and then to find the missing side):

1) Scale Factor = New length ÷ Old length = 13.2 ÷ 8.4 = 1.57
2) New width = Scale Factor × Old width = 1.57 × 5.8 = 9.1 cm

BUT WITHOUT THE FORMULA TRIANGLE YOU'RE SCUPPERED!

The Acid Test:

LEARN the FOUR KEY FEATURES of enlargements, especially the FORMULA TRIANGLE.

Then, when you think you know it, cover the page and write it all down again, from memory, including the sketches and examples, especially the photo enlargement one. Keep trying till you can.

Symmetry

SYMMETRY is where a shape or picture can be put in DIFFERENT POSITIONS that LOOK EXACTLY THE SAME. There are THREE TYPES of symmetry:

1) Line Symmetry

This is where you can draw a MIRROR LINE (or more than one) across a picture and both sides will fold exactly together.

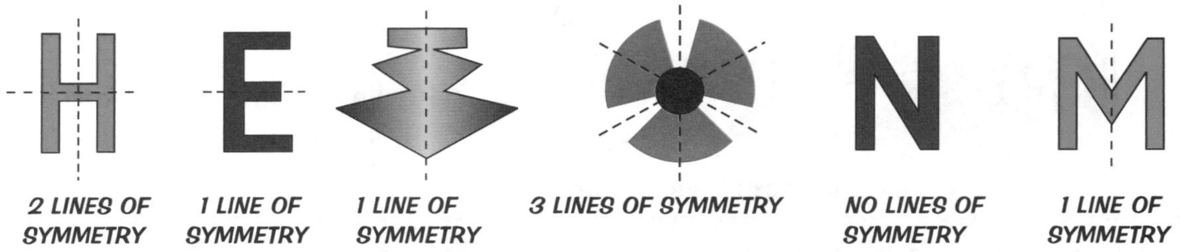

How to draw a reflection:

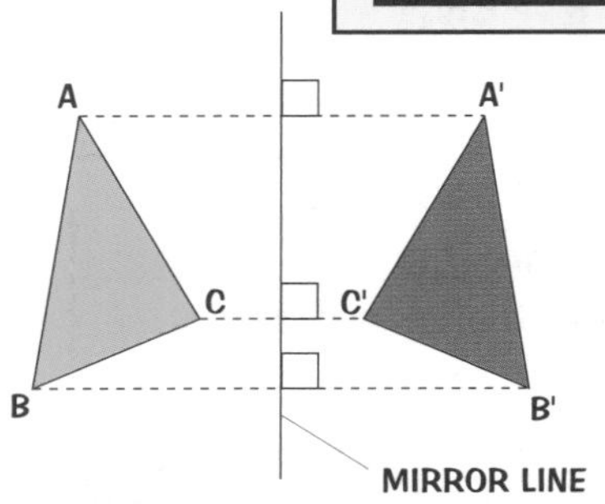

1) Reflect each point one by one
2) Use a line which crosses the mirror line at 90° and goes *EXACTLY the same distance* on the other side of the mirror line, as shown.

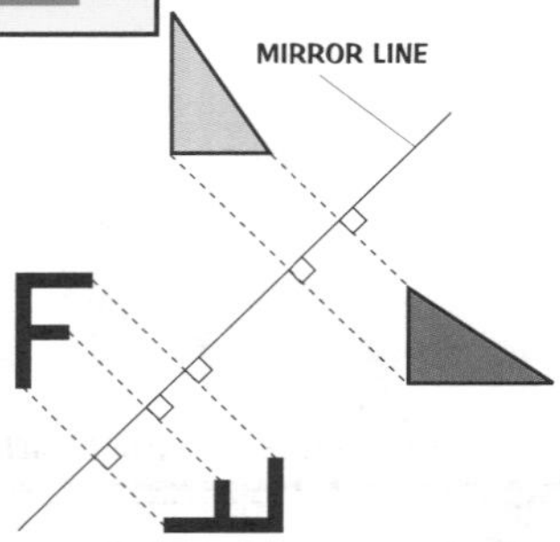

2) Plane Symmetry

Plane Symmetry is all to do with 3-D SOLIDS.
Whereas flat shapes can have a mirror line,
solid 3-D objects can have planes of symmetry.

A plane mirror surface can be drawn through many regular solids, but the shape must be EXACTLY THE SAME ON BOTH SIDES OF THE PLANE (i.e. mirror images), like these are:

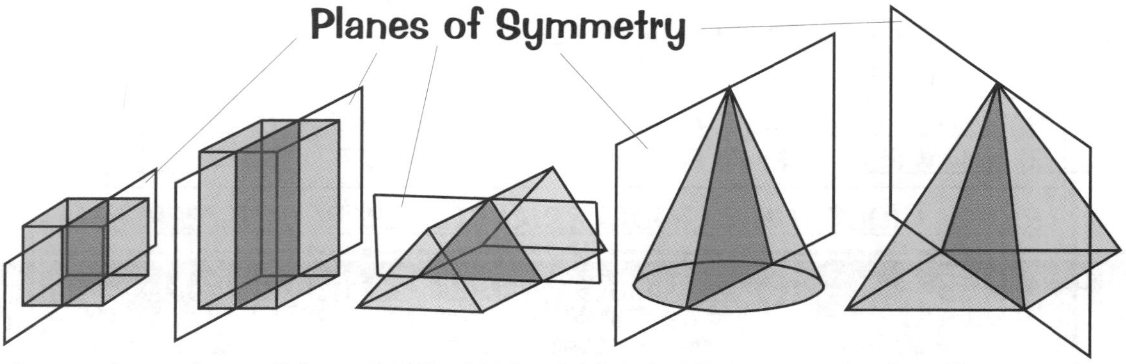

The shapes drawn here all have MANY MORE PLANES OF SYMMETRY but there's only one drawn in for each shape, because otherwise it would all get really messy and you wouldn't be able to see anything.

Symmetry

3) Rotational Symmetry

This is where you can ROTATE the shape or drawing into different positions that all look exactly the same.

Order 1 Order 2 Order 2 Order 3 Order 4

Two Key Points:

1) The ORDER OF ROTATIONAL SYMMETRY is the fancy way of saying: "HOW MANY DIFFERENT POSITIONS LOOK THE SAME".
e.g. you should say the Z shape above has "Rotational symmetry order 2"

2) BUT... when a shape has ONLY 1 POSITION you can EITHER say that it has "Rotational Symmetry order 1" OR that it has "NO Rotational Symmetry".

Tracing Paper

SYMMETRY IS ALWAYS A LOT EASIER WITH TRACING PAPER.

1) For REFLECTIONS, trace one side of the drawing and the mirror line too. Then TURN THE PAPER OVER and line up the mirror line in its original position again.
(If you put a blob on the mirror line it helps you get it back in position again)

2) For ROTATIONS, just swizzle the tracing paper round.
It's really good for finding the CENTRE of rotation (by trial and error) as well as the order of rotational symmetry.

3) You can use tracing paper in the EXAM — so ASK FOR IT, or else take your own in with you.

The Acid Test:

LEARN the important details about LINE AND PLANE SYMMETRY, the 2 points about ROTATIONAL SYMMETRY and the 3 points about TRACING PAPER.

Now TURN OVER and WRITE IT ALL DOWN *with examples*, to see what you've learned.

1) Copy these letters and mark in all the lines of symmetry.
Also say what the rotational symmetry is for each one.
H N E Y M O S T

2) Copy all the five solids on the last page without their plane of symmetry.
Then draw in a different plane of symmetry for each one.
(Drawing 3-D objects ain't easy but it's good laughing at everyone else's dismal efforts.)

The Shapes You Need To Know

These are easy marks in the Exam — make sure you know them all.

1) SQUARE

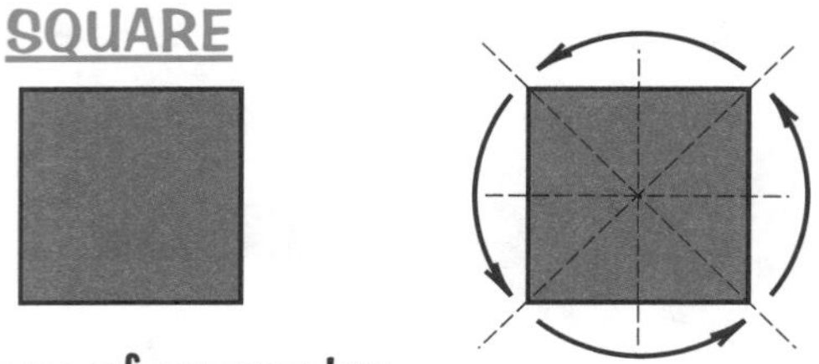

4 lines of symmetry.
Rotational symmetry order 4

2) RECTANGLE

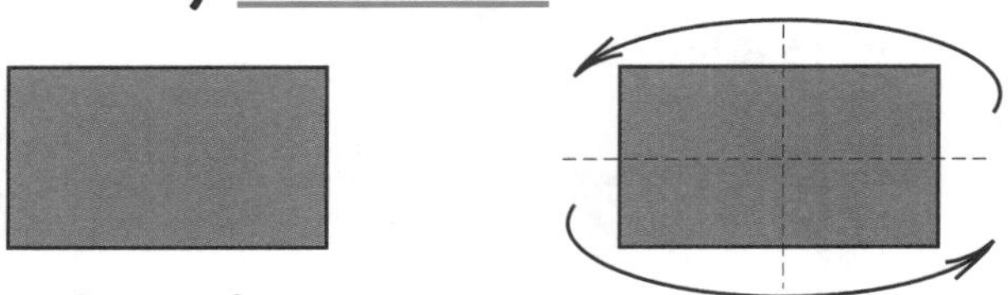

2 lines of symmetry.
Rotational symmetry order 2

3) RHOMBUS (A square pushed over)
(It's also a diamond)

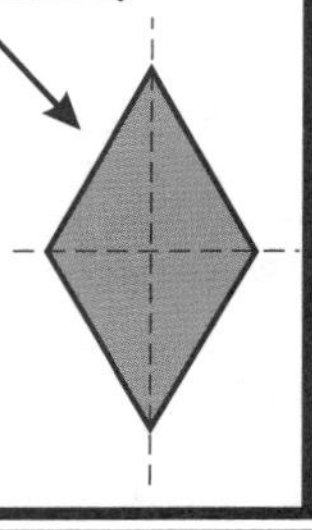

2 lines of symmetry.
Rotational symmetry order 2

4) PARALLELOGRAM
(A rectangle pushed over — two pairs of parallel sides)

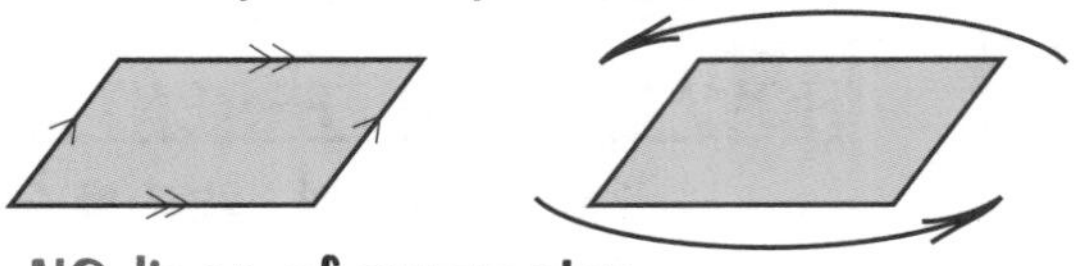

NO lines of symmetry.
Rotational symmetry order 2

5) TRAPEZIUM (One pair of parallel sides)

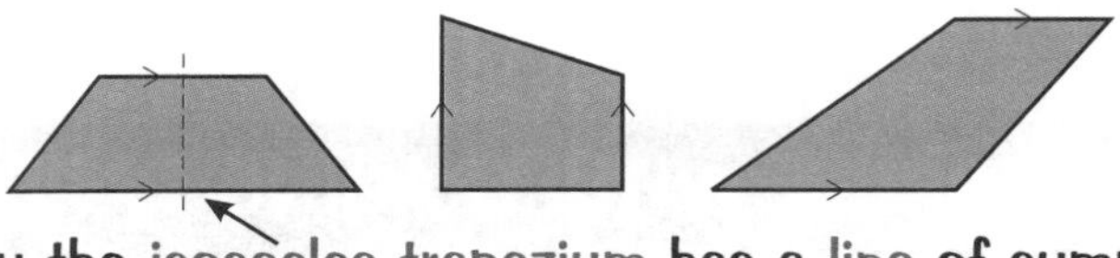

Only the isosceles trapezium has a line of symmetry.
None have rotational symmetry

6) KITE

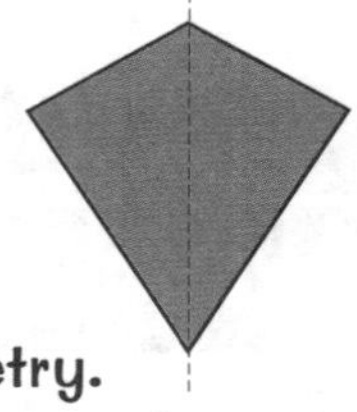

1 line of symmetry.
No rotational symmetry

7) EQUILATERAL Triangle

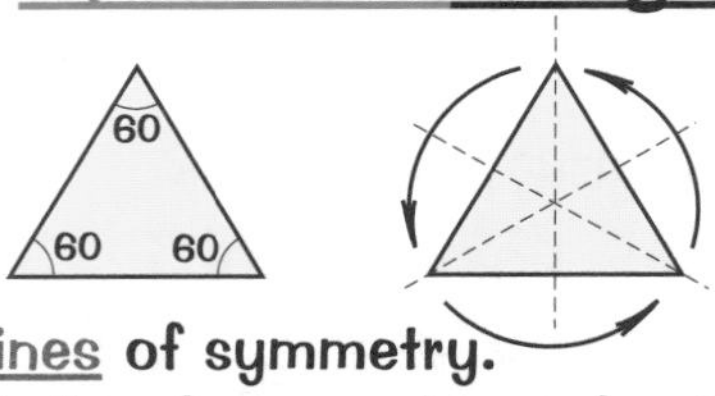

3 lines of symmetry.
Rotational symmetry order 3

8) RIGHT-ANGLED Triangle

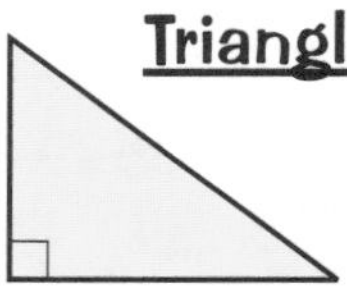

No symmetry unless the angles are 45°

9) ISOSCELES Triangle

2 sides equal
2 angles equal

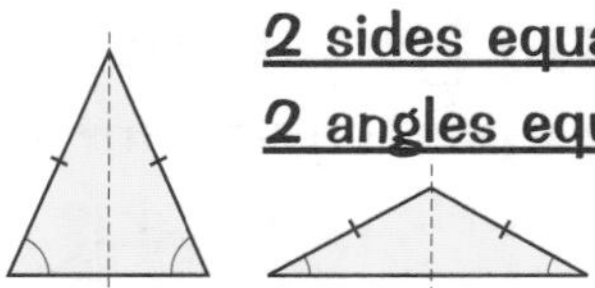

1 line of symmetry.
No rotational symmetry

10) SOLIDS

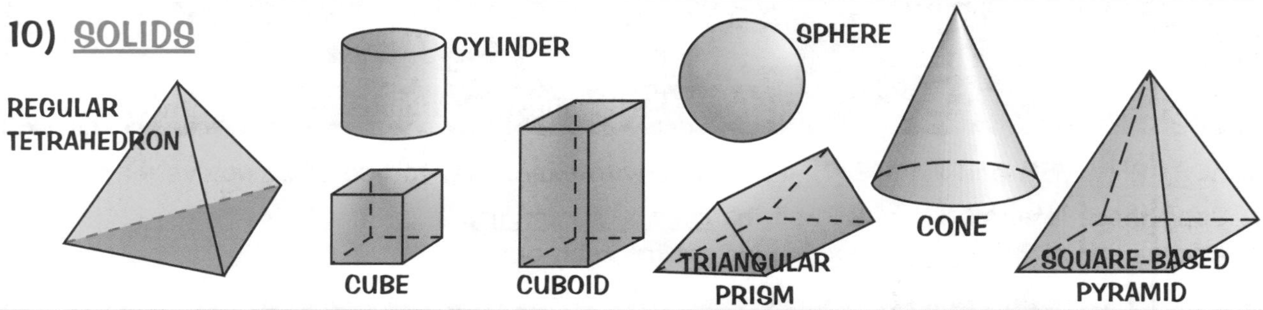

The Acid Test:

LEARN everything on this page.

Then turn over and write down all the details that you can remember. Then try again.

Areas

YES IT'S TRUE, these formulae are given inside the front cover of the Exam, but I **GUARANTEE** that if you don't learn them beforehand, you'll be *totally incapable* of using them in the Exam — *REMEMBER, I ABSOLUTELY GUARANTEE IT*!

You must LEARN these Formulae:

1) RECTANGLE

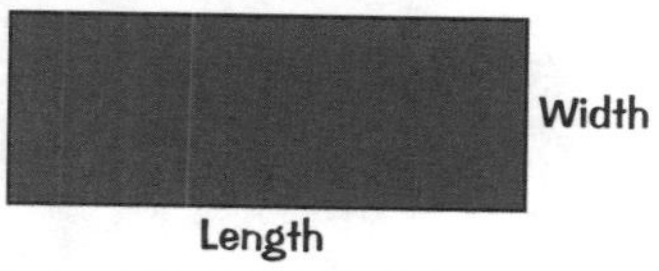

Area of *RECTANGLE* = length × width

$$A = l \times w$$

2) TRIANGLE

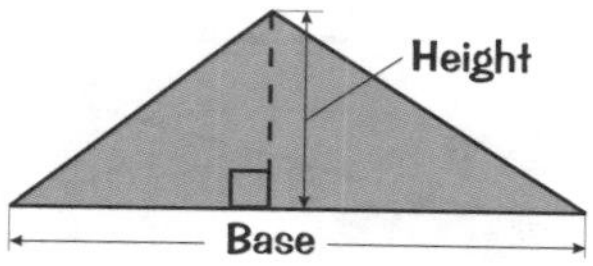

Area of *TRIANGLE* = ½ × base × vertical height

$$A = \tfrac{1}{2} \times b \times h_v$$

Note that the *height* must always be the *vertical height*, not the sloping height.

3) PARALLELOGRAM

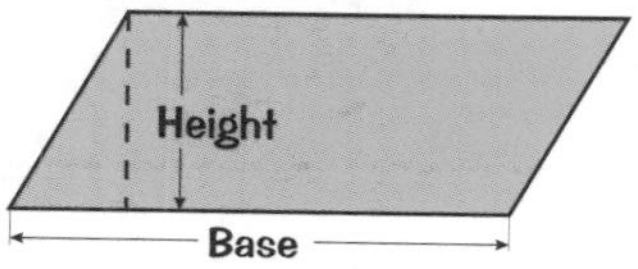

Area of *PARALLELOGRAM* = base × vertical height

$$A = b \times h_v$$

4) TRAPEZIUM

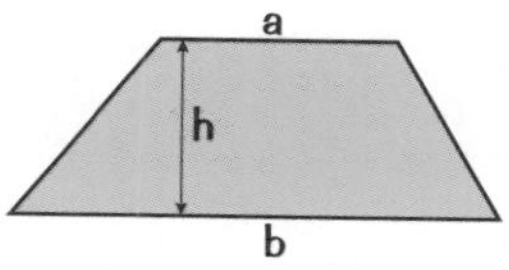

Area of *TRAPEZIUM* = average of parallel sides × distance between them

$$A = \tfrac{1}{2} \times (a + b) \times h$$

5) CIRCLE

π = 3.141592....
= 3.14 (approx)

Circumference = distance round the outside of the circle

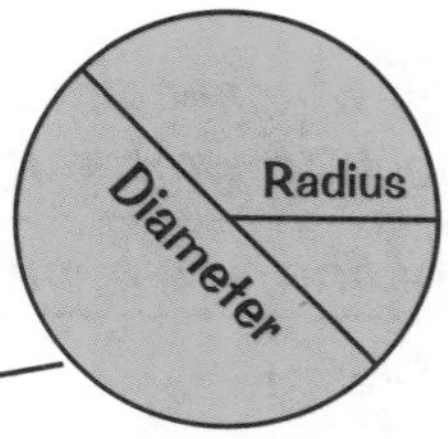

DON'T MUDDLE UP THESE TWO CIRCLE FORMULAE!

AREA of *CIRCLE* = π × (radius)^2

$$A = \pi \times r^2$$

e.g. if the radius is 4cm, then A = 3.14×(4×4) = 50.24cm^2

CIRCUMFERENCE = π × Diameter

$$C = \pi \times D$$

YOU NEED TO KNOW WHAT THESE ARE TOO:

5a) SECTOR OF CIRCLE

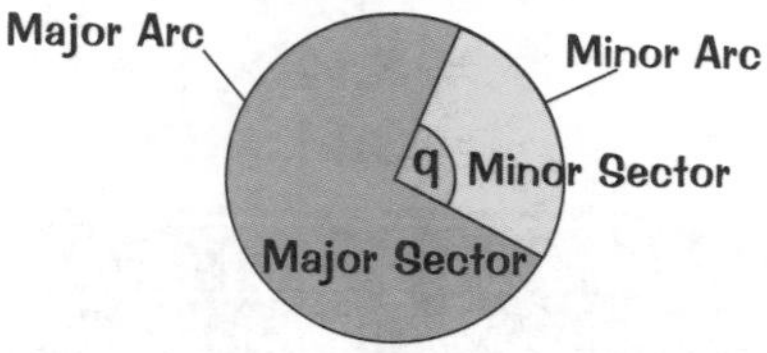

5b) SEGMENT OF CIRCLE

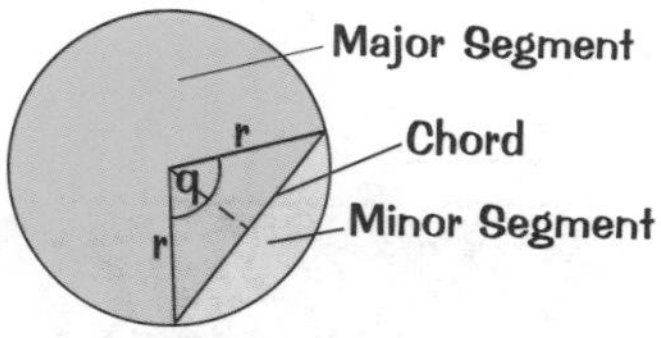

The Acid Test:

LEARN THIS PAGE — then COVER THE PAGE AND WRITE DOWN as much of it as you can FROM MEMORY.

Check your effort and try again!

Circle Questions

1) π "A Number a Bit Bigger than 3"

The big thing to remember is that π (called "pi") only seems confusing because it's a scary-looking Greek letter. In the end, it's just an ordinary number (3.14159...) which is rounded off to either 3 or 3.14 or 3.142 (depending on how accurate you want to be). And that's all it is: *A NUMBER A BIT BIGGER THAN 3*.

2) Diameter is TWICE the Radius

The *DIAMETER* goes right across the circle.
The *RADIUS* only goes *halfway* across.

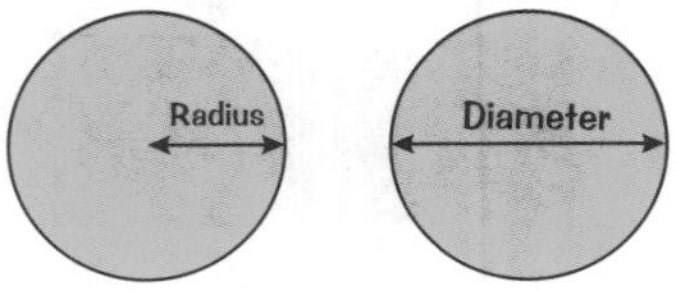

EXAMPLES:

If the radius is 4cm, the diameter is 8cm, If D = 12cm, then r = 6cm,
If the radius is 12m, the diameter is 24m, If diameter = 2mm, then radius = 1mm

3) Arc, Chord and Tangent

A TANGENT is a straight line that just touches the outside of the circle.

A CHORD is a line drawn across the inside of a circle.

AN ARC is just part of the circumference of the circle.

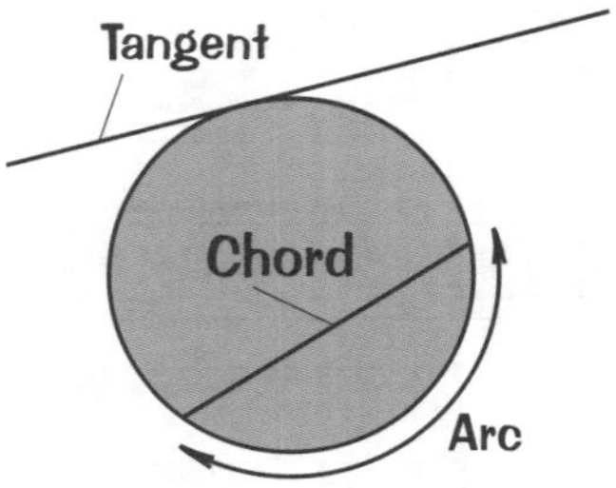

4) The Big Decision:

"Which circle formula do I use?"

WORKING OUT AREA OR CIRCUMFERENCE — there is a difference you know!

1) If the question asks for "the area of the circle",

YOU MUST use the FORMULA FOR AREA: $A = \pi \times r^2$

2) If the question asks for "circumference" (the distance around the circle)

YOU MUST use the FORMULA FOR CIRCUMFERENCE: $C = \pi \times D$

AND REMEMBER, it makes no difference at all whether the question gives you the radius or the diameter, because it's dead easy to work out one from the other.

EXAMPLE: "Find the circumference and the area of the circle shown below."

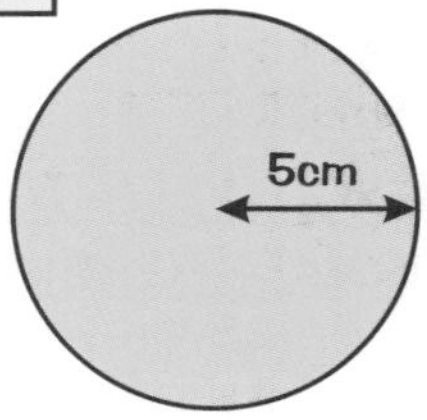

ANSWER: Radius = 5 cm, so Diameter = 10 cm (easy)

Formula for CIRCUMFERENCE is:
$C = \pi \times D$, so
$C = 3.14 \times 10$
$= 31.4$ cm

Formula for AREA is:
$A = \pi \times r^2$
$= 3.14 \times (5\times5)$
$= 3.14 \times 25 = 78.5\text{ cm}^2$

The Acid Test:

There are 4 SECTIONS on this page. They're all mighty important — LEARN THEM.

Now cover the page and *write down* everything you've learnt. Frightening isn't it.

1) A plate has a diameter of 14cm. Find the area and the circumference of it using the methods you've just learnt. Remember to show all your working out.
2) A flower bed has a radius of 6m. Find the area and circumference of it.

Perimeters and Areas

1) Perimeters of Complicated Shapes

Make sure you know these nitty gritty details about perimeter:

1) Perimeter is the distance *all the way around the outside of a 2-D shape*.

2) To find a PERIMETER, you ADD UP THE LENGTHS OF ALL THE SIDES, but....
THE ONLY RELIABLE WAY to make sure you get *all the sides* is this:

> 1) Put a big blob at one corner and then go around the shape.
> 2) Write down the length of every side as you go.
> 3) Even sides that seem to have no length given — you must *work them out*.
> 4) Keep going until you get back to the BIG BLOB.

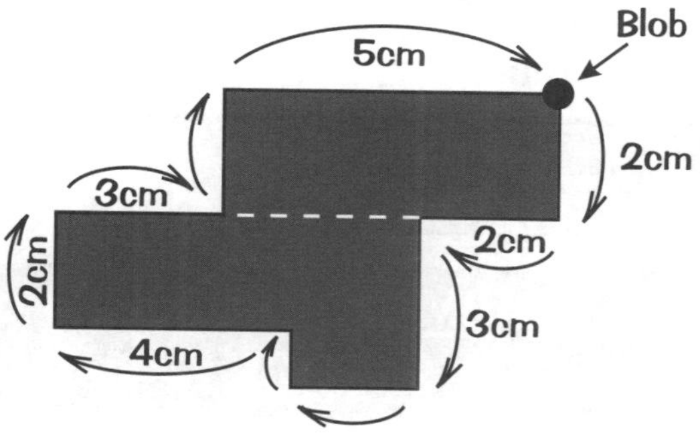

e.g. 2+2+3+2+1+4+2+3+2+5 = 26 cm

Yes, I know you think it's yet another fussy method, but believe me, it's so easy to miss a side. You must use GOOD RELIABLE METHODS for EVERYTHING — or you'll lose marks willy nilly.

2) Areas of Complicated Shapes

> 1) SPLIT THEM UP into *the 3 basic shapes*: RECTANGLE, TRIANGLE, AND CIRCLE.
> 2) Work out the area of each bit SEPARATELY.
> 3) Then ADD THEM ALL TOGETHER (or sometimes SUBTRACT them).

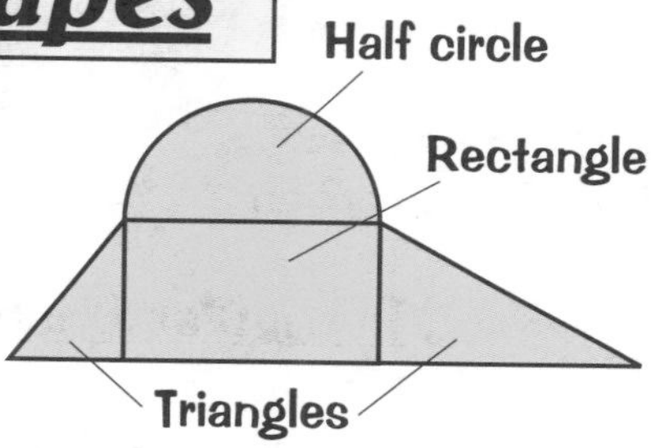

EXAMPLE: *Work out the area of this shape:*

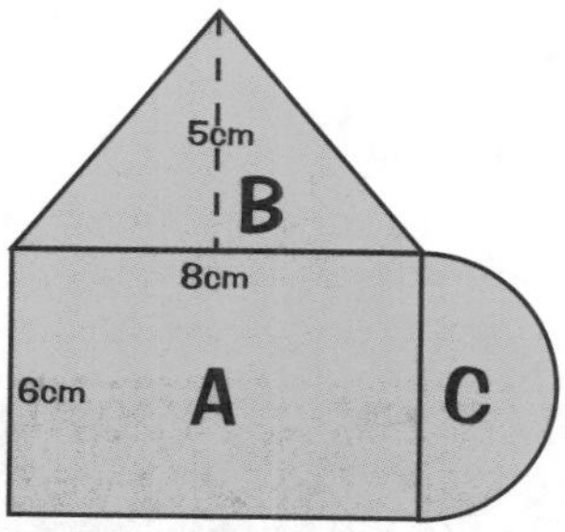

ANSWER:

Rectangle A:

Area = l × w
= 8 × 6
= 48 cm²

Triangle B:

Area = ½×b×h
= ½×8×5
= 20 cm²

Semicircle C:

Area = $(\pi \times r^2) \div 2$
= $(3.14 \times 3^2) \div 2$
= 14.13 cm²

TOTAL AREA = 48 + 20 + 14.13 = 82.13 cm²

The Acid Test:

LEARN THE RULES for finding the perimeter and area of complicated shapes.

1) *Turn over and write down* what you've learnt.

2) Find the perimeter and area of the shape shown here:

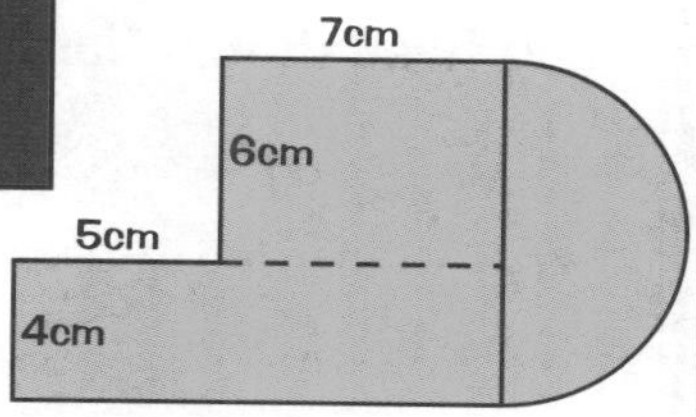

Volume or Capacity

VOLUMES — YOU MUST LEARN THESE!

1) CUBOID (RECTANGULAR BLOCK)

(This is also known as a '*rectangular prism*' — see below to understand why)

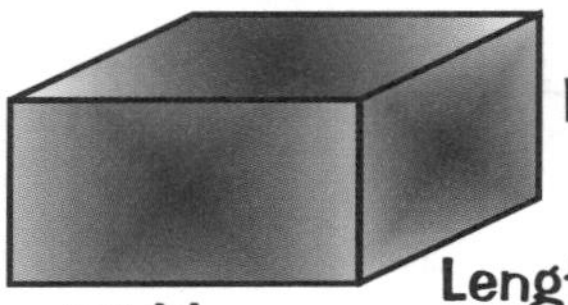

Volume of Cuboid = length × width × height

$$V = l \times w \times h$$

(The other word for volume is *CAPACITY*)

2) PRISM

A PRISM is a solid (3-D) object which has a CONSTANT AREA OF CROSS-SECTION — i.e. it's the same shape all the way through.

Now, for some reason, not a lot of people know what a prism is, but they come up all the time in Exams, so make sure YOU know.

Circular Prism

(or Cylinder)

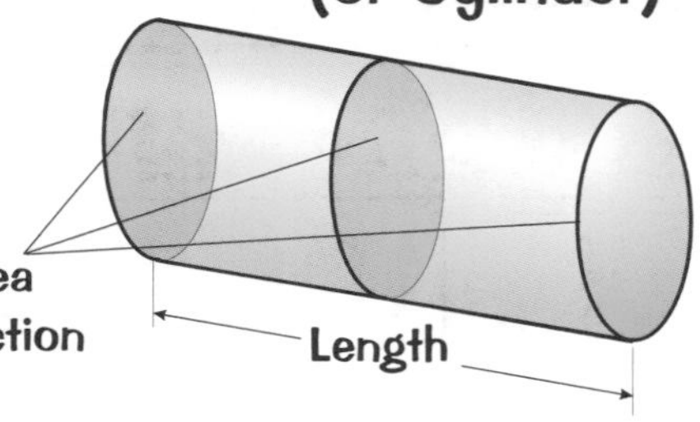

Hexagonal Prism

(a flat one, certainly, but still a prism)

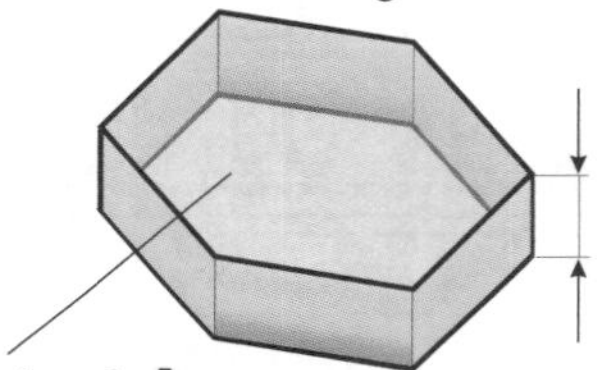

Triangular Prism

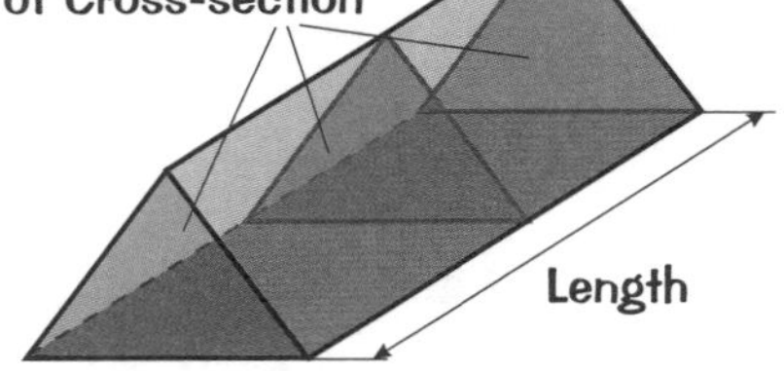

Volume of prism = Cross-sectional Area × length

$$V = A \times l$$

As you can see, the formula for the volume of a prism is *very simple*. The *difficult* part, usually, is *finding the area of the cross-section*.

The Acid Test:

LEARN this page. Then turn over and try to write it all down. Keep trying until you can do it.

Practise these two questions until you can do them all the way through without any hesitation. Name the shapes and find their volumes:

a)

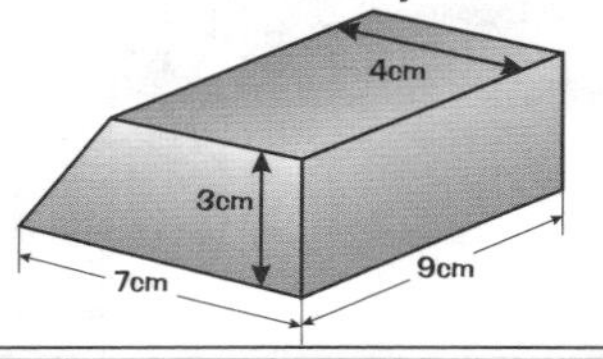

b)

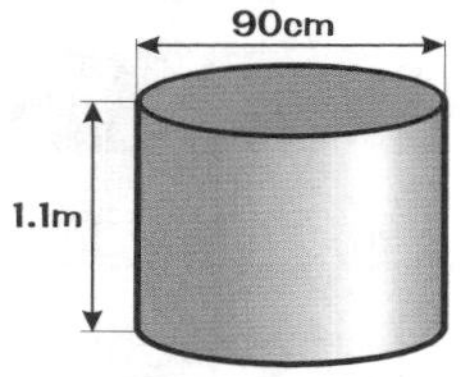

Solids and Nets

You need to know what Face, Edge and Vertex mean:

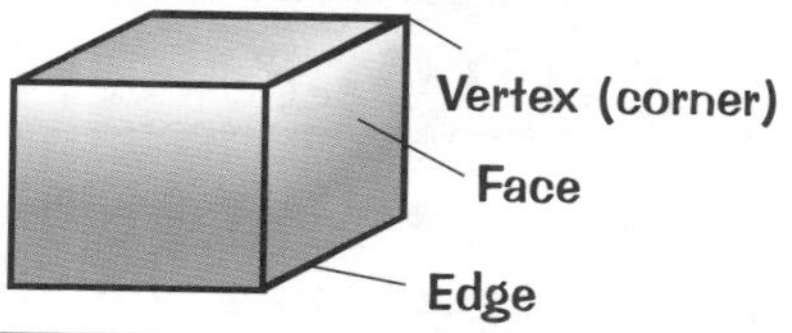

Surface Area and Nets

1) SURFACE AREA only applies to solid 3-D objects, and it's simply *the total area of all the outer surfaces added together*. If you were painting it, it's all the bits you'd paint!
2) There is never a simple formula for surface area — *you have to work out each side in turn and then* ADD THEM ALL TOGETHER.
3) A NET is just A SOLID SHAPE FOLDED OUT FLAT.
4) So obviously: SURFACE AREA OF SOLID = AREA OF NET.

There are 4 nets that you need to know really well for the Exam, and they're shown below. They may well ask you to draw one of these nets and then work out its area.

1) Triangular Prism

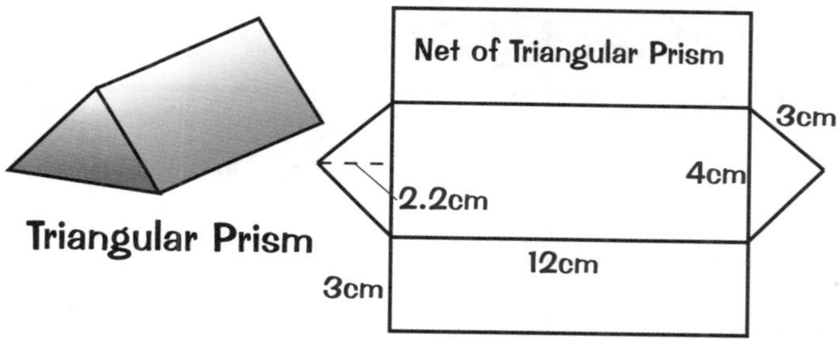

2) Cube

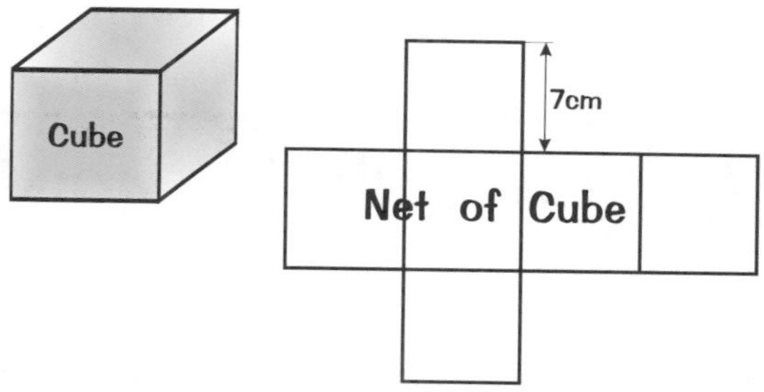

3) Cuboid

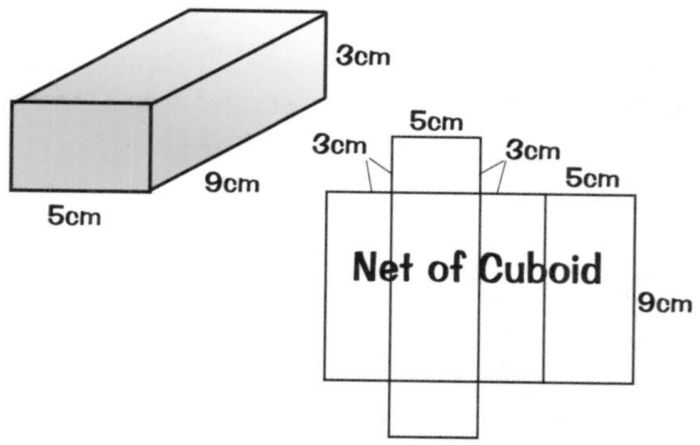

4) Pyramid

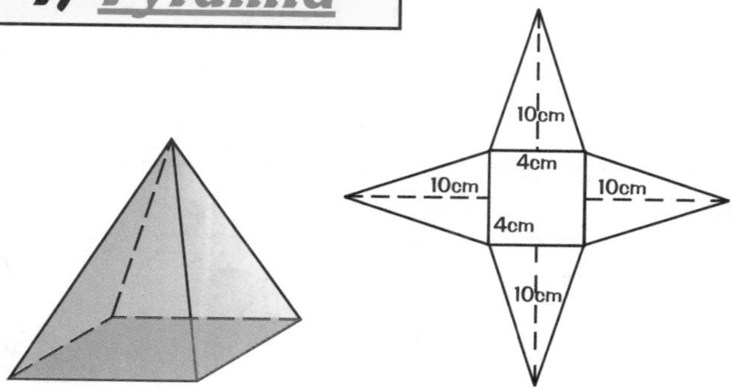

Square-based Pyramid

Net of Square-based Pyramid

The Acid Test:

LEARN the 4 details on surface area and nets and the FOUR NETS on this page, and also the little diagram at the top of the page.

Now cover the page and write down everything you've learnt.

1) Work out the area of all four nets shown above.

Geometry

8 Simple Rules — that's all:

If you know them ALL — THOROUGHLY, you at least have a fighting chance of working out problems with lines and angles. *If you don't — you've no chance*.

1) Angles in a triangle

Add up to 180°.

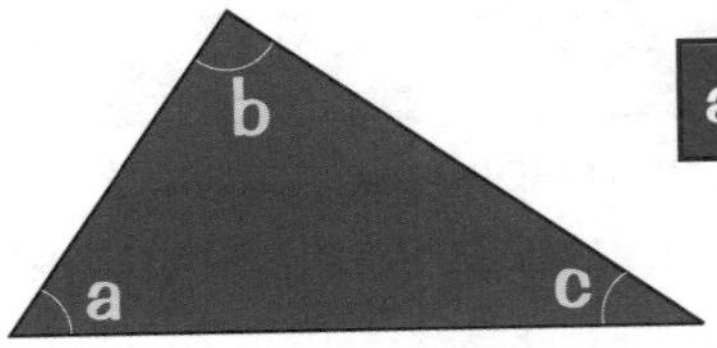

$a+b+c=180°$

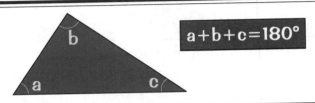

2) Angles on a straight line

Add up to 180°.

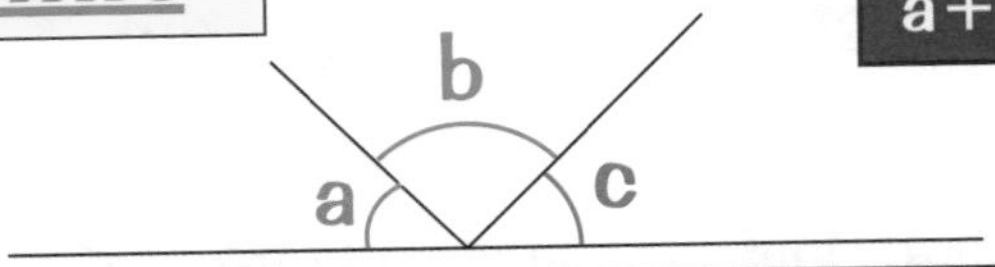

$a+b+c=180°$

3) Angles in a 4-sided shape

(a "Quadrilateral")

Add up to 360°.

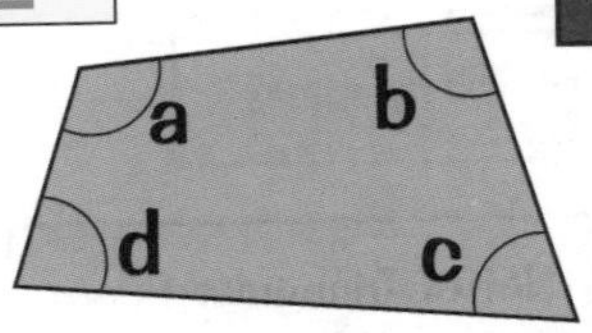

$a+b+c+d=360°$

4) Angles round a point

Add up to 360°.

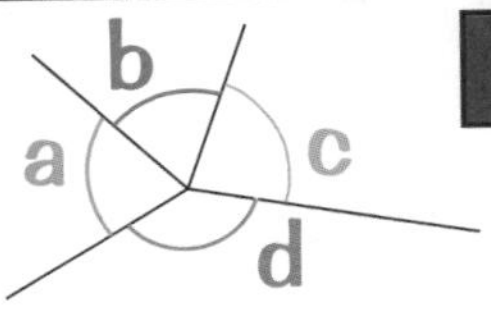

$a+b+c+d=360°$

5) Exterior Angle of Triangle

Exterior Angle of triangle
= sum of Opposite Interior angles

i.e. $a+b=d$

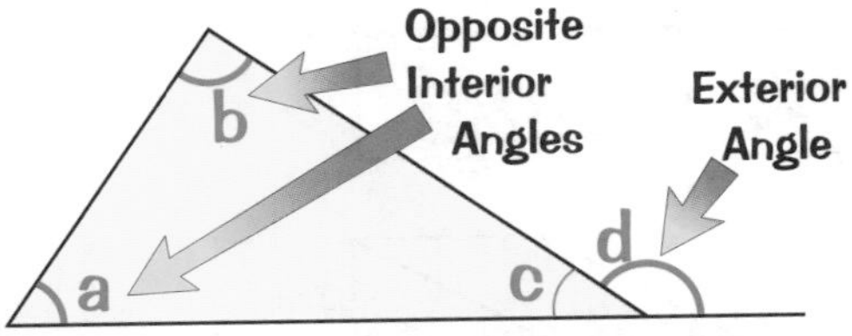

6) Isosceles triangles

2 sides the same
2 angles the same

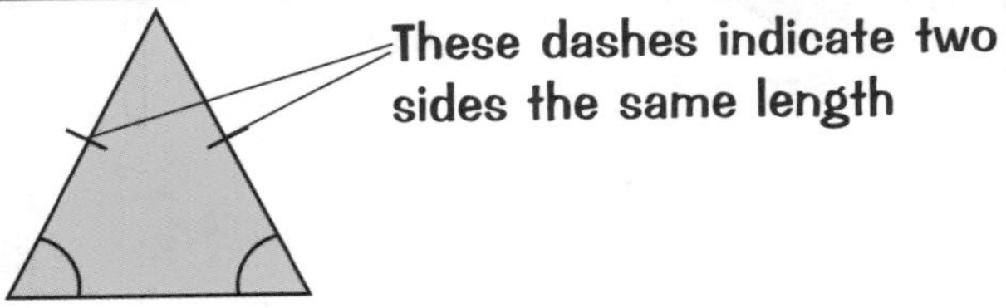

In an isosceles triangle, *YOU ONLY NEED TO KNOW ONE ANGLE* to be able to find the other two, which is *very useful IF YOU REMEMBER IT*.

a)

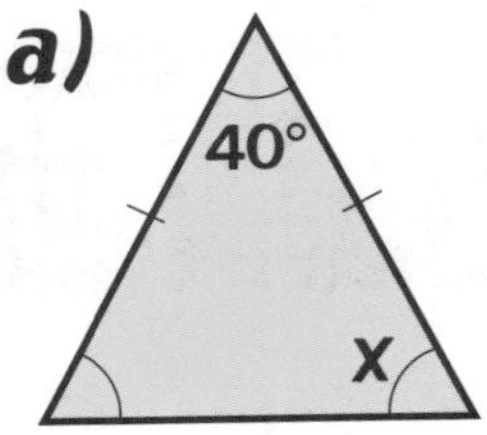

180° – 40° = 140°
The two bottom angles are both the same and they must add up to 140°, so each one must be half of 140° (= 70°). So X = 70°.

b)

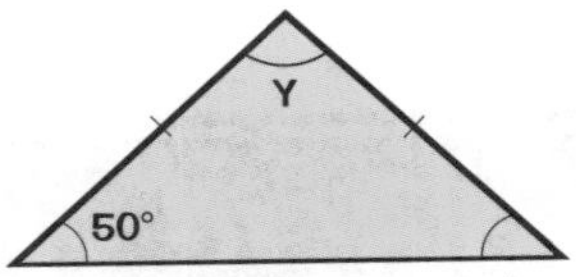

The two bottom angles must be the same, so 50° + 50° = 100°.
All the angles add up to 180° so Y = 180° – 100° = 80°.

Geometry

7) Parallel lines

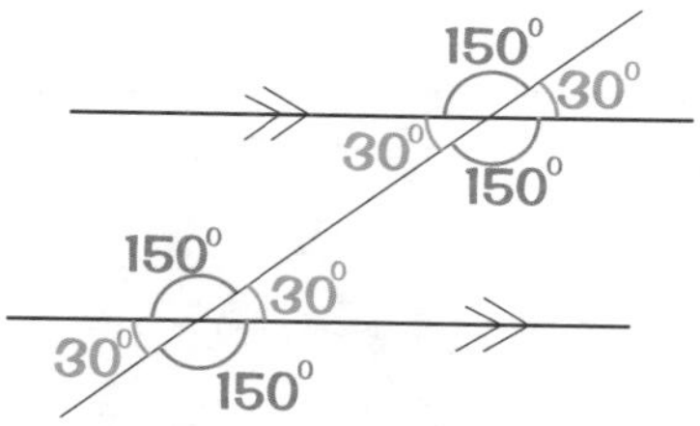

Whenever one line goes across 2 parallel lines, then the two bunches of angles are the same (The arrows mean those 2 lines are parallel)

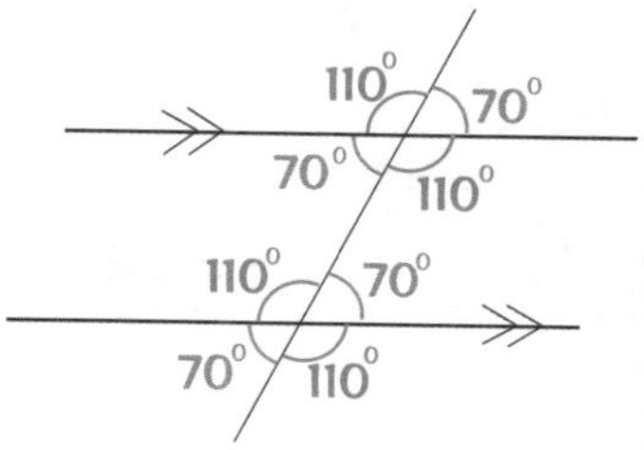

Whenever you have TWO PARALLEL LINES there are *only two different angles*: A SMALL ONE and A BIG ONE and they ALWAYS ADD UP TO 180°.
E.g. 30° and 150° or 70° and 110°

The trickiest bit about parallel lines is spotting them in the first place — watch out for these "Z", "C", "U" and "F" shapes popping up:

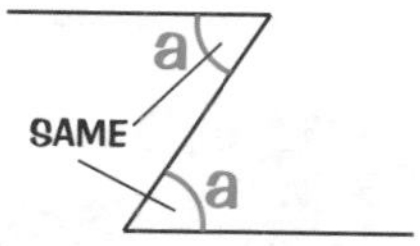

In a Z-shape they're called "ALTERNATE ANGLES"

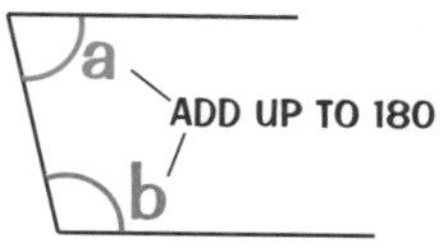

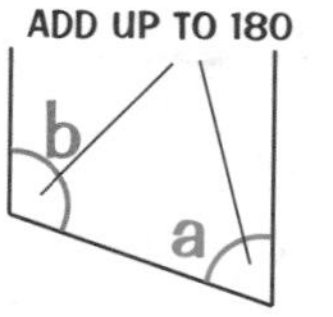

If they add up to 180 they're called "SUPPLEMENTARY ANGLES"

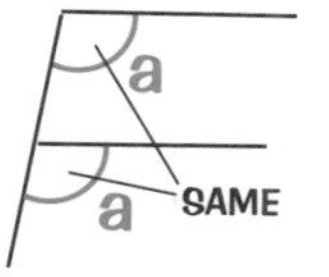

In an F-shape they're called "CORRESPONDING ANGLES"

If necessary, EXTEND THE LINES to make the diagram easier to get to grips with:

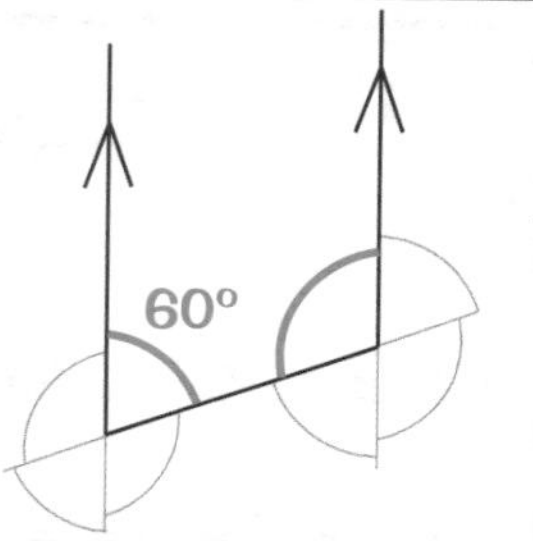

8) Irregular Polygons: Interior and Exterior Angles

An irregular polygon is basically any shape with lots of straight sides which aren't all the same length. There are two formulas you need to know:

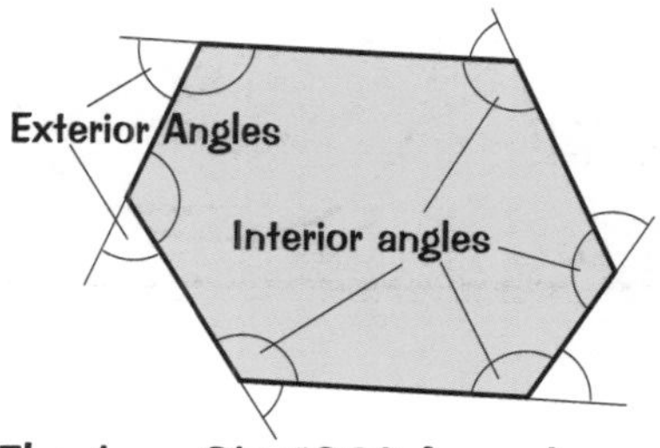

Sum of Exterior angles = 360°

Sum of Interior angles = (n – 2)×180°
where n is the number of sides

The (n – 2)×180° formula comes from splitting the inside of the polygon up into triangles using full diagonals. Each triangle has 180° in it so just count up the triangles and times by 180°. There's always 2 less triangles than there are sides, hence the (n – 2).

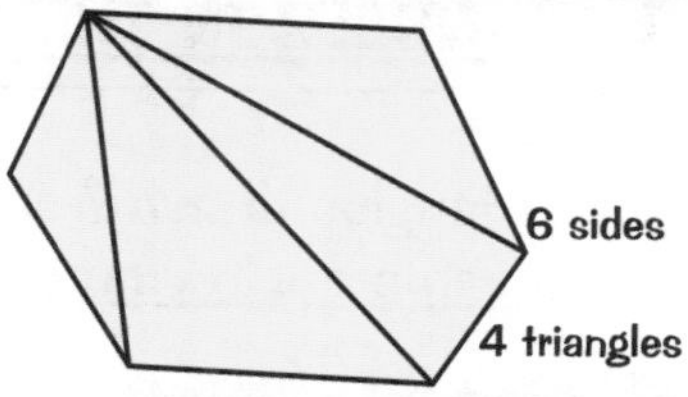

The Acid Test:

LEARN EVERYTHING on these two pages. Then turn over and see how much of it you can write down.

1) Find the size of angle Z in the triangle shown:
2) How much do the exterior angles of a 7-sided polygon add up to?
3) How much do the interior angles of a 5-sided polygon add up to?
4) One of the diagrams above has one angle given as 60°. Find the other 7 angles.

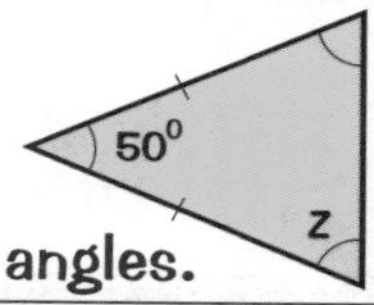

Circle Geometry

Nine Simple Rules — that's all:

You'll have to learn these too if you want to be able to do circle problems.

1) ANGLE IN A SEMICIRCLE = 90°

A triangle drawn from the two ends of a diameter will ALWAYS make an angle of 90° where it hits the edge of the circle, no matter where it hits.

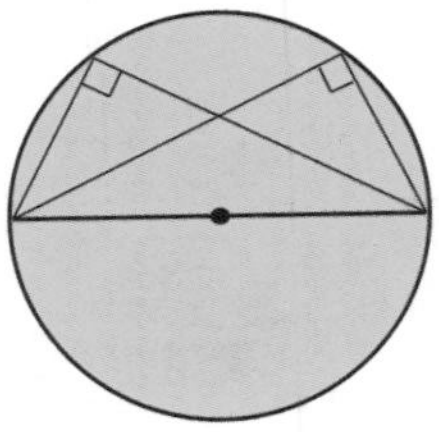

2) TANGENT and RADIUS MEET AT 90°

A TANGENT is a line that just touches the edge of a curve. If a tangent and radius meet at the same point, then the angle they make is *EXACTLY 90°*.

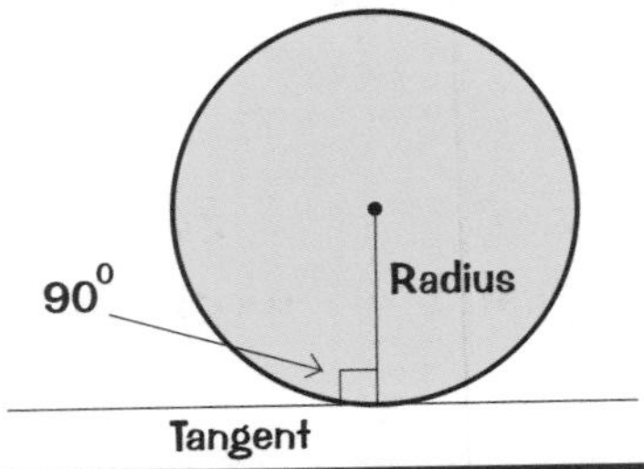

3) SNEAKY ISOSCELES TRIANGLES FORMED BY TWO RADII

Unlike other isosceles triangles they don't have the little tick marks on the sides to remind you that they're the same — the fact that two sides are radii is enough to make it an isosceles trangle.

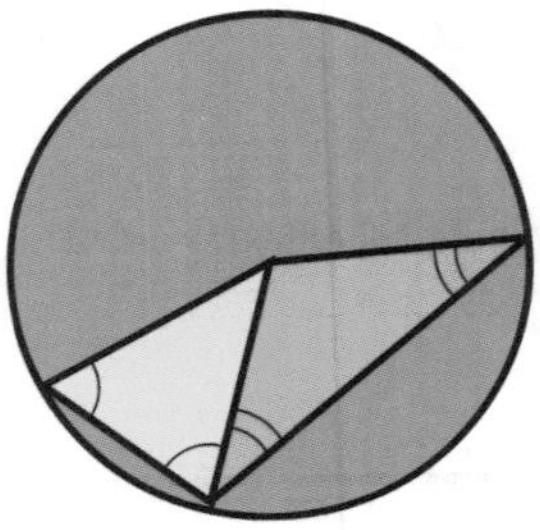

4) CHORD BISECTOR IS A DIAMETER

A CHORD is any line drawn across a circle, and no matter where you draw a chord, the line that cuts it exactly in half (at 90°), will go through the centre of the circle and so it'll have to be a *DIAMETER*.

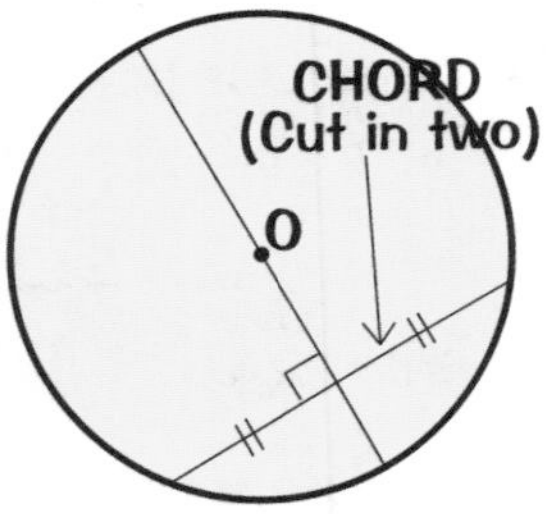

5) ANGLES IN THE SAME SEGMENT ARE EQUAL

All triangles drawn from a chord will have the same angle where they touch the circle.

Also, the two angles on opposite sides of the chord add up to 180°.

When the chord chops the circle in half (to form 2 semicircles), the angle at the edge of the circle is always a right angle.

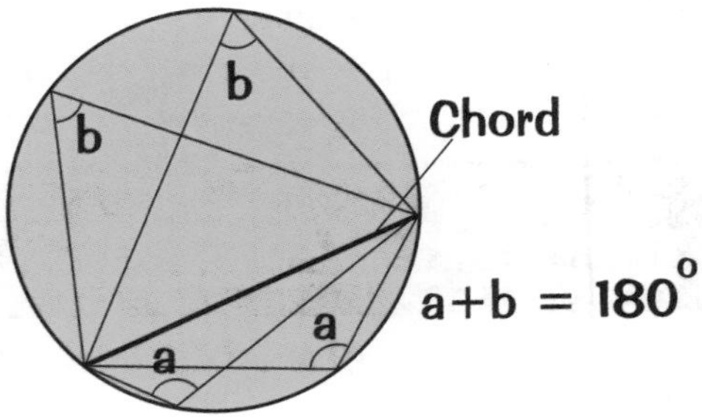

Circle Geometry

6) ANGLE AT THE CENTRE IS TWICE THE ANGLE AT THE EDGE

The angle subtended at the centre of a circle is EXACTLY DOUBLE the angle subtended at the edge of the circle from the same two points (two ends of the same chord). The phrase "angle subtended at" is nothing complicated, it's just a bit posher than saying "angle made at".

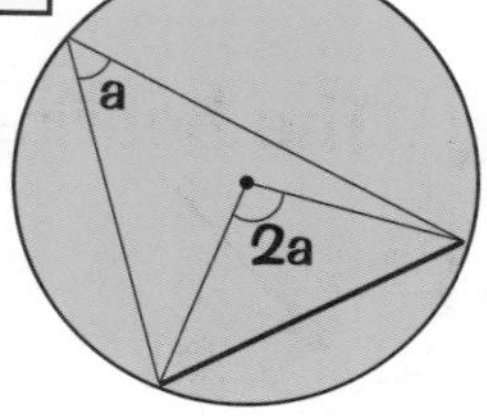

7) OPPOSITE ANGLES OF A CYCLIC QUADRILATERAL ADD UP TO 180°

$a+c=180°$

$b+d=180°$

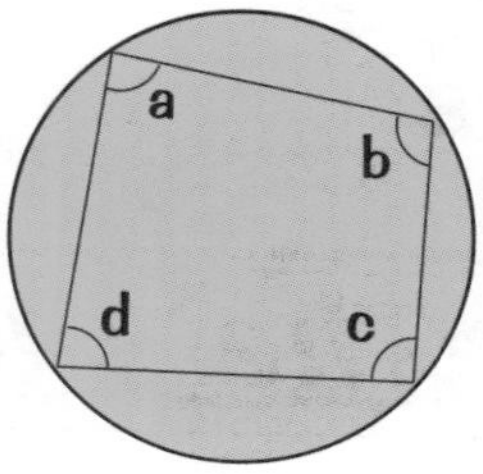

A *cyclic quadrilateral* is a 4-sided shape with every corner touching the circle. Both pairs of opposite angles add up to 180°.

8) EQUALITY OF TANGENTS FROM A POINT

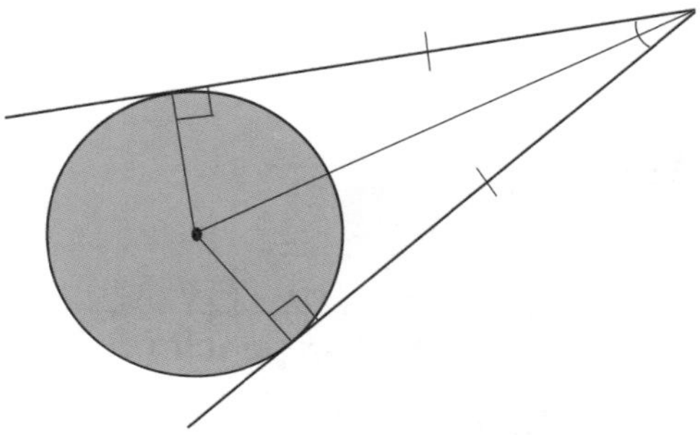

The two tangents drawn from an outside point are always equal in length, so creating an "isosceles" situation, with two congruent right-angled triangles.

9) ANGLE IN OPPOSITE SEGMENT IS EQUAL

This is perhaps the trickiest one to remember. If you draw a tangent and a chord that meet, then the angle between them is always equal to *"the angle in the opposite segment"* (i.e. the angle made at the edge of the circle by two lines drawn from the chord)

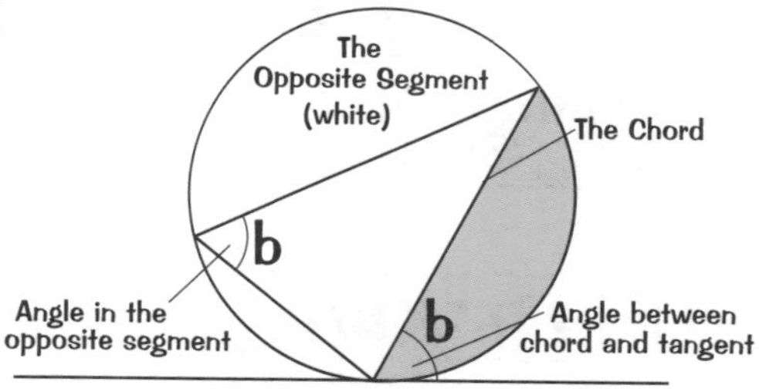

10) WHEN YOU'RE STUCK...

It's all too easy to find yourself staring at a geometry problem and getting nowhere — IF SO, this is what you do:

GO THROUGH ALL THE 17 RULES OF GEOMETRY (on pages 80-83), ONE BY ONE, and APPLY EACH OF THEM IN TURN in as many ways as possible — *ONE OF THEM IS BOUND TO WORK.*

In other words, just find *ALL* the angles in whichever order they become obvious.

The Acid Test: LEARN all Nine Rules on these two pages, and all 8 from the last two pages. Then turn over and write them all down.

Check your effort and try again — and keep trying till you can do it!

Bearings

Bearings — 3 Key Points

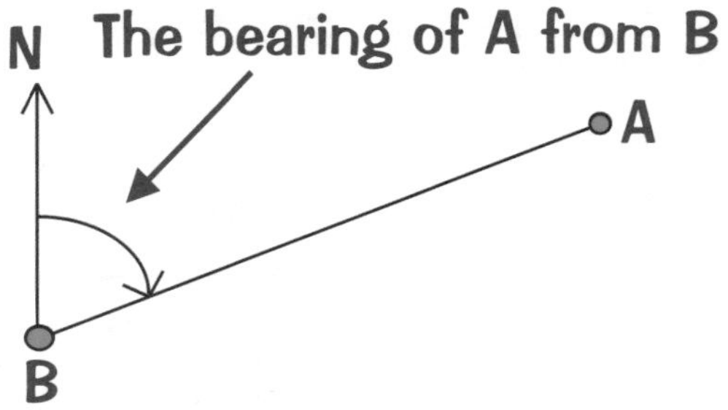

1) A bearing is the DIRECTION TRAVELLED between two points, GIVEN AS AN ANGLE in degrees.
2) All bearings are measured CLOCKWISE from the NORTHLINE.
3) All bearings should be given as 3 figures, e.g. 243°, 060° (not 60°), 008° (not 8°), 018° etc.

The 3 Key Words

Only learn this if you want to get bearings *RIGHT*

1) "FROM"

Find the word "FROM" in the question, and put your pencil on the diagram at the point you are going *"from"*.

2) NORTHLINE

At the point you are going "FROM", *draw in a* NORTHLINE.

3) CLOCKWISE

Now draw in the angle CLOCKWISE *from the northline to the line joining the two points*. This angle is the BEARING.

Example

Find the bearing of Q from P:

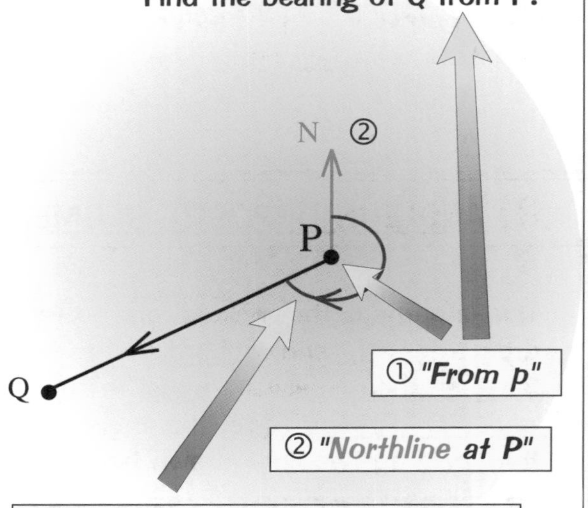

This angle is the bearing of Q from P and is 245°.

The Acid Test:

LEARN the 3 Features of Bearings and the 3 Key Steps of the method for finding them.

Now turn over and write down what you've just learnt.
Keep trying till you can write down all six points from memory.

1) Find the bearing of H from T. (Use a protractor)
2) Find the bearing of T from H.

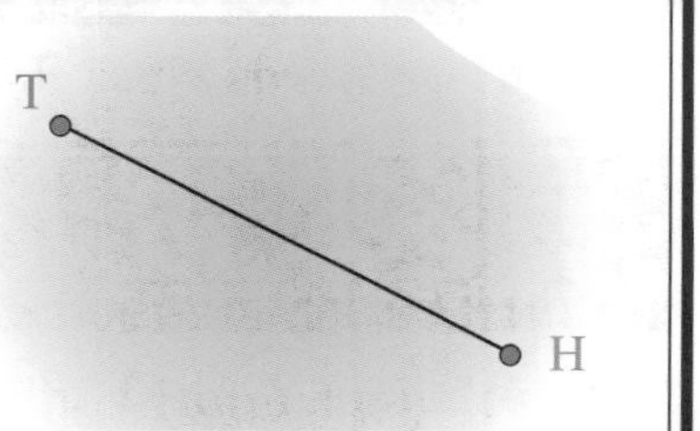

Vectors

SOME MONSTROUSLY IMPORTANT THINGS you need to know about vectors:

1) A VECTOR is just a certain length in a certain direction

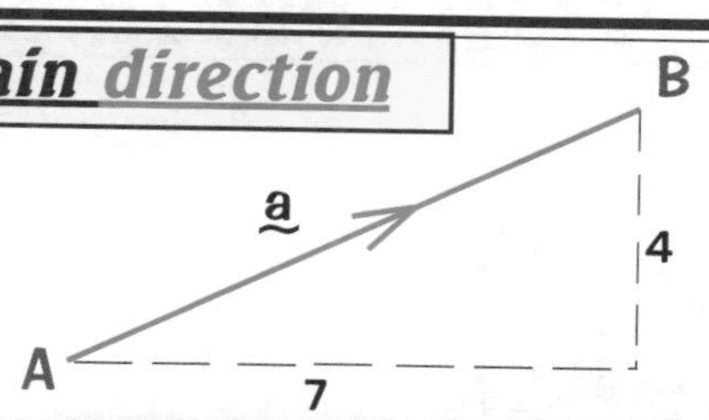

1) Vectors are *always* shown as lines with arrows on them.
2) The length and direction of the line represent the size and direction of the thing in question.
3) There are *four notations* you need to know. The vector shown above can be referred to as either:

$\begin{pmatrix}7\\4\end{pmatrix}$ or $\underset{\sim}{a}$ or **a** (in bold type) or $\overrightarrow{AB}$

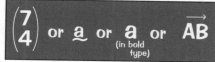

2) What Exactly are Vectors?

VECTORS HAVE BOTH SIZE AND DIRECTION — and you're supposed to remember that.

"*But what is a vector?*" I hear you cry.

Well vectors represent *real-life things* which have SIZE and DIRECTION: you know, things like *position*, *velocity*, *acceleration*, *force* — things that are not only *big or small*, but also *act in a certain direction*.

(Temperature on the other hand, is *NOT a vector*, because it only has a value, e.g. 80°C, — it never points in a certain direction as well.)

So these arrows you keep dealing with are supposed to represent something real like a velocity or a force, etc.

Fortunately you only need to learn these simple rules to be able to do vector questions — but it's kind of nice to know they're not *completely* irrelevant really, isn't it!

3) Column Vectors

1) The notation for column vectors is: $\begin{pmatrix}x \rightarrow\\y \uparrow\end{pmatrix}$, i.e. two numbers in brackets,

   where: Top number = distance moved in the + X-direction (→)
   Bottom number = distance moved in the + Y-direction (↑).

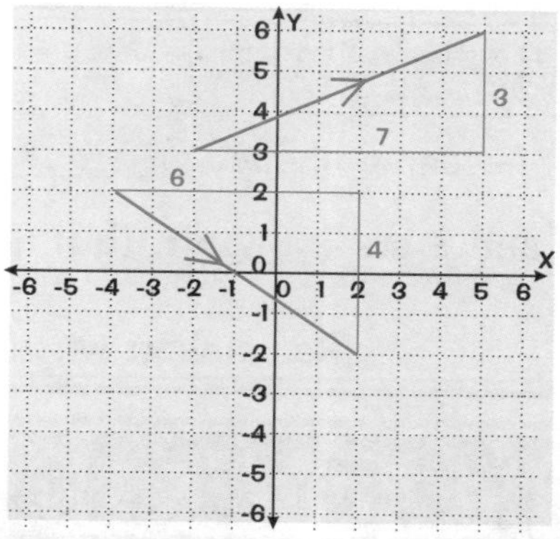

2) Make sure you get the x and y the right way round.

   The two vectors shown are $\begin{pmatrix}7\\3\end{pmatrix}$ and $\begin{pmatrix}6\\-4\end{pmatrix}$

3) Also note that moving ← way or ↓ way will mean a negative number in the column vector, like the –4 in the one above.

The Acid Test:

LEARN this page. There are several important points in each of the 3 sections — LEARN THEM ALL.

1) Now cover up the page and write down all you know about vectors, including the 4 notations, the 3 rules for column vectors and 4 examples of real-life vectors.

Projections, Congruence and Similarity

Projections show the Scale of the Shape

A '*projection*' shows the relative size and shape of an object from either the *front*, *side* or *back* — they're usually known as '*elevations*'. A '*plan*' shows the view from *above*. They're always *drawn to scale*.

Take this church (naff picture, I know) — you can represent it like this:

FRONT Elevation — the view you'd see if you looked from directly *in front*:

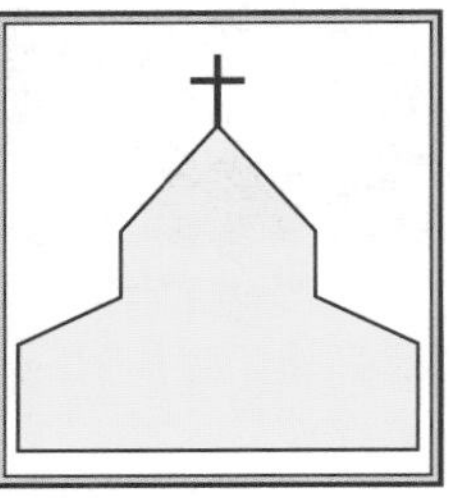

SIDE Elevation — the view you'd see if you looked from directly to *one side*:

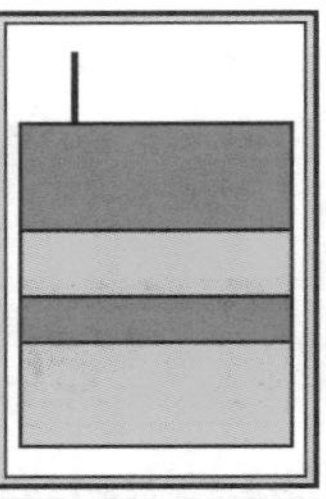

PLAN — the view you'd see if you looked from directly *above*:

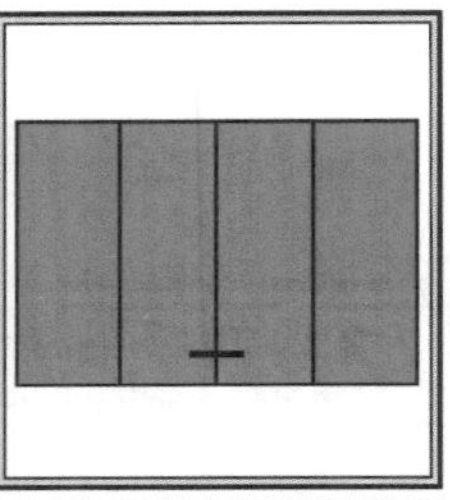

If they're feeling really mean (and they often are), you might get a question on:

ISOMETRIC Projection — this is where the shape is drawn (again, to scale) from a view at *equal angles to* all three axes (*x, y and z*). Or more simply, it's a drawing like this:

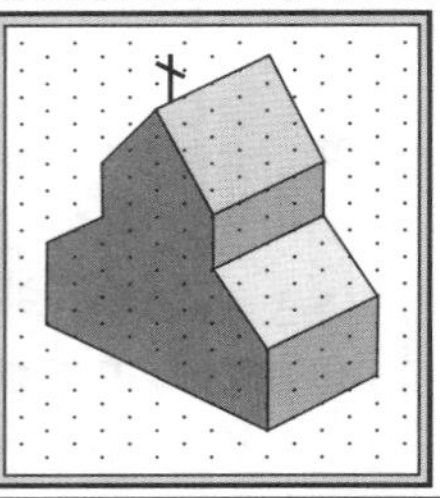

This one's a bit trickier, so you might want to spend a little longer practising it — just to get your head round it.

Congruence and Similarity

Congruence is another ridiculous maths word which sounds really complicated when it's not: If two shapes are *CONGRUENT*, they're simply *the same* — *the same size and the same shape*.

CONGRUENT

— same size, same shape

A, B, and C are CONGRUENT (with each other)

SIMILAR

— same shape, *different size*

D and E are SIMILAR, (but not congruent)

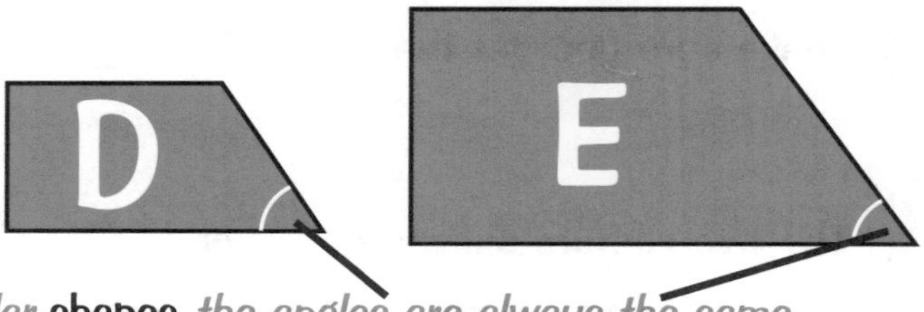

Remember: when you have *similar* shapes *the angles are always the same*.

The Acid Test: Make sure you understand ALL FOUR TYPES OF PROJECTION, and LEARN exactly what "SIMILAR" and "CONGRUENT" mean.

Now cover the page and write down what you've learned. Then REMEMBER it forever!

1) Draw a plan, front and side elevations and an isometric projection of your own house.

2) a) Which of these four shapes are similar?
   b) Which are congruent?

i) ii) iii) iv)

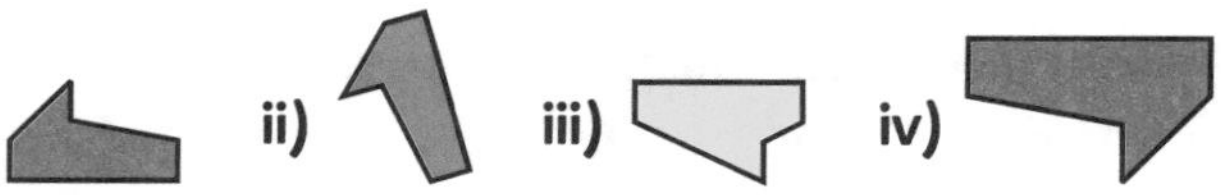

Trigonometry

Using formula triangles to do Trigonometry makes the whole thing *a whole lot easier*, but ALWAYS follow all these steps in this order. If you miss any out you're asking for trouble.

Method

Using SIN, COS and TAN to solve right-angled triangles

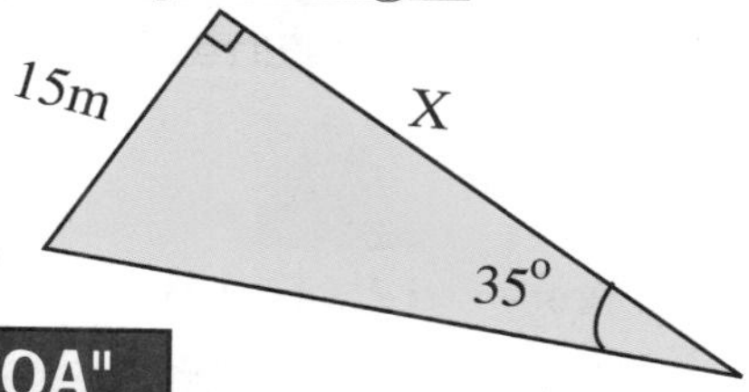

1) Label the three sides O, A and H

(Opposite, Adjacent and Hypotenuse).

2) Write down FROM MEMORY "SOH CAH TOA"

(Sounds like a Chinese word, "Sockatoa!")

3) Decide WHICH TWO SIDES are involved O,H A,H or O,A

and select SOH, CAH or TOA accordingly

4) Turn the one you choose into a FORMULA TRIANGLE, thus:

S O H   C A H   T O A

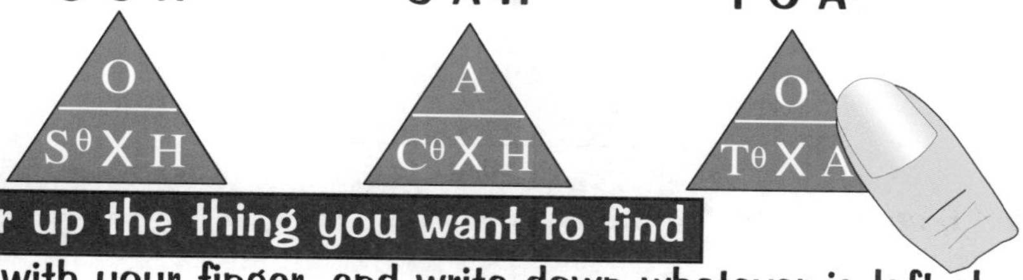

5) Cover up the thing you want to find

with your finger, and write down whatever is left showing.

6) Translate into numbers and work it out

7) Finally, check that your answer is sensible.

Seven Nitty Gritty Details

- The HYPOTENUSE is the LONGEST SIDE.
  The OPPOSITE is the side OPPOSITE the angle being used (θ).
  The ADJACENT is the side NEXT TO the angle being used (θ).
- θ IS A GREEK LETTER called "theta", *and is used to represent ANGLES*
- In the formula triangles, S^{θ} represents SIN θ, C^{θ} is COS θ ,and T^{θ} is TAN θ.
- On some calculators, you have to enter trig functions BACKWARDS.
  So for SIN 45 you might have to press [45] [SIN] (but most calculators do it the right way now).
- Remember, TO FIND THE ANGLE — USE INVERSE (see next page).
- ALWAYS USE A DIAGRAM — *draw your own if necessary.*
- You can only use SIN, COS and TAN on RIGHT-ANGLED TRIANGLES — you may have to *add lines to the diagram to create one* — especially on ISOSCELES triangles.

The Acid Test:

LEARN the 7 Steps of the Method and....
...the 7 Nitty Gritty Details.

Then turn over and write them all down from memory.

Trigonometry

Example 1)

"Find x in the triangle shown."

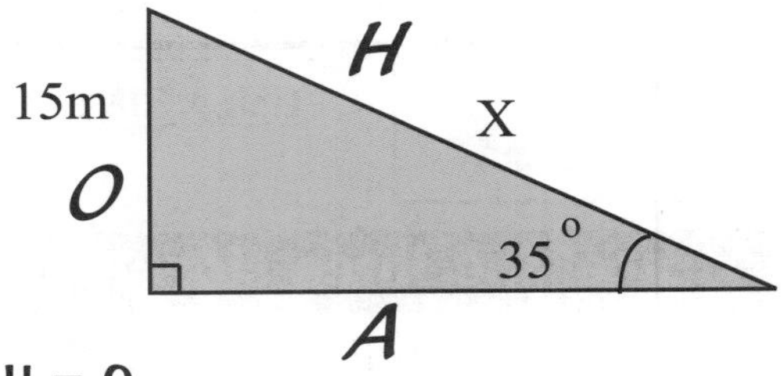

1) Label O,A,H
2) Write down "SOH CAH TOA"
3) Two sides *involved*: O,H
4) So use 

5) We want to find H so cover it up to leave: $H = O / S^{\theta}$
6) Substitute in values: $X = 15 / \text{SIN } 35$

Press 15 ÷ SIN 35 = 26.151102

So answer = **26.2m**

7) Check it's sensible: yes it's about twice as big as 15, as the diagram suggests.

Example 2)

"Find the angle θ in this triangle."

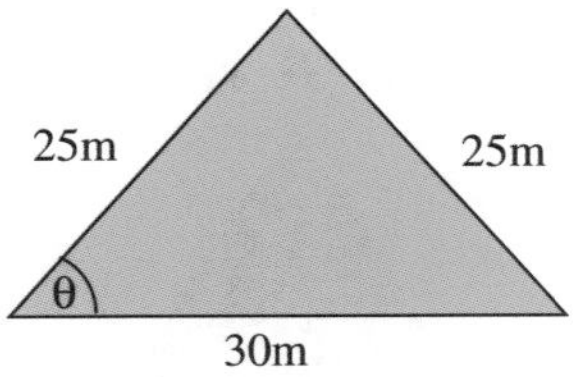

Note the usual way of dealing with an ISOSCELES TRIANGLE: split it down the middle to get a RIGHT ANGLE:

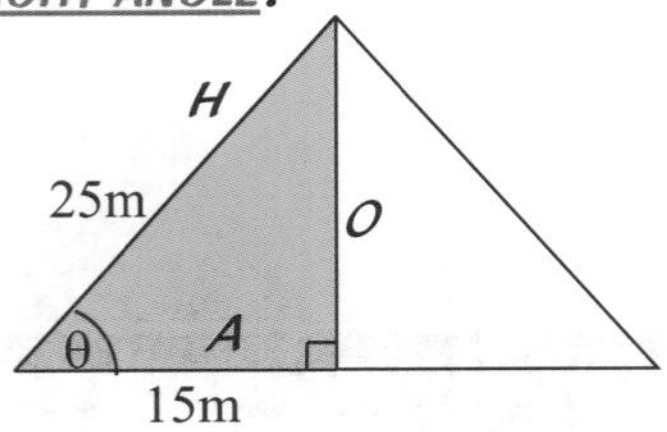

1) Label O, A, H
2) Write down "SOH CAH TOA"
3) Two sides involved: A,H
4) So use 

5) We want to find θ so cover up Cθ to leave: $C\theta = A / H$
6) Substitute in values: $\text{COS } \theta = 15 / 25 = 0.6$

NOW USE INVERSE : $\theta = \text{INV COS } (0.6)$

Press INV COS 0.6 = 53.130102

So ans. = **53.1°**

7) Finally, is it sensible? — Yes, the angle looks like about 50°.

Angles of Elevation And Depression

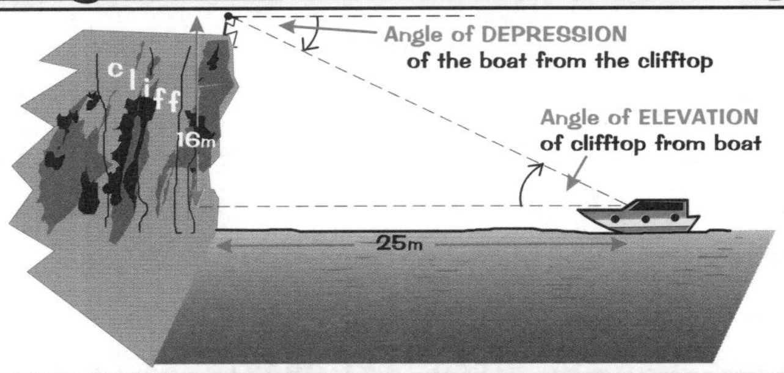

1) The *Angle of Depression* is the angle *downwards* from the horizontal.

2) The *Angle of Elevation* is the angle *upwards* from the horizontal.

3) The *Angle of Elevation* and *Angle of Depression* are *ALWAYS EQUAL*.

The Acid Test:

Practise these questions until you can apply the method fluently and without having to refer to it at all.

1) Find X

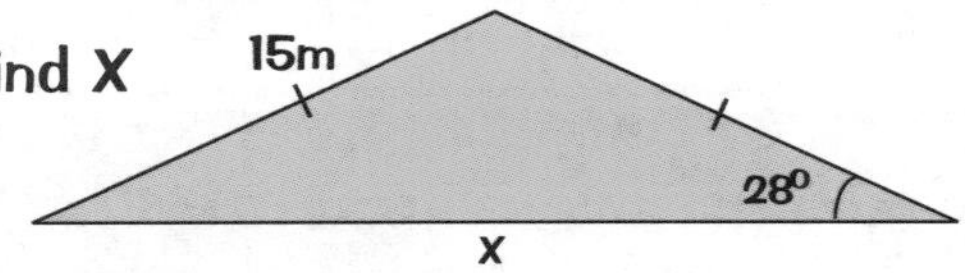

2) Find θ

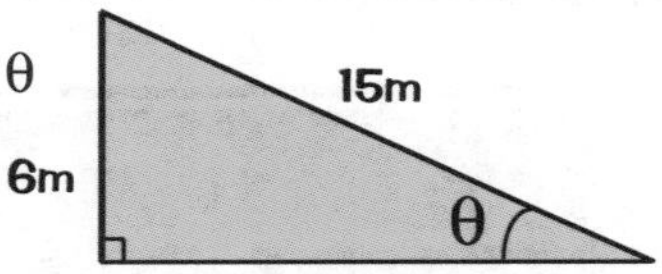

3) Calculate the angles of elevation and depression in the boat drawing above.

Pythagoras' Theorem

1) PYTHAGORAS' THEOREM goes hand in hand with SIN, COS and TAN because they're both involved with RIGHT ANGLED TRIANGLES.
2) The big difference is that PYTHAGORAS DOES NOT INVOLVE ANY ANGLES — it just uses *two sides* to find the *third side*. (SIN, COS and TAN always involve ANGLES)

Method

The basic formula for Pythagoras' theorem is : $a^2 + b^2 = h^2$

Remember that Pythagoras can only be used on RIGHT-ANGLED TRIANGLES.

The trouble is, the formula can be quite difficult to use. *Instead*, it's a lot better to *just remember* these *THREE SIMPLE STEPS*, which work every time:

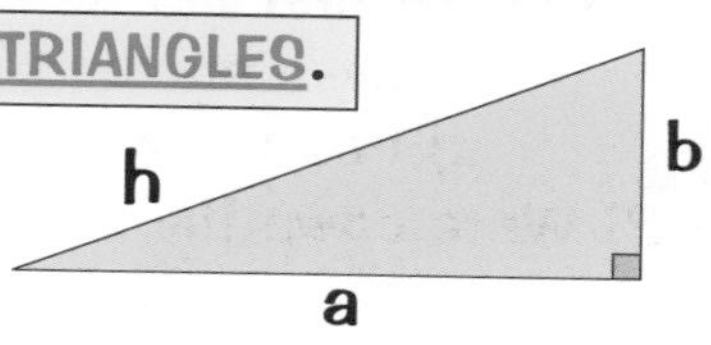

1) Square Them

SQUARE THE TWO NUMBERS that you are given,
(use the x^2 button if you've got your calculator — if you haven't, make sure you know the squares on P.19)

2) Add or Subtract

To find the *longest side*, ADD the two squared numbers.
To find *a shorter side*, SUBTRACT the smaller one from the larger.

3) Square Root

Once you've got your answer, take the SQUARE ROOT.
(By pressing $\sqrt{\ }$, then checking that your answer is SENSIBLE, or by *remembering everything on P.20.*)

Example 1: *"Find the missing side in the triangle shown."*

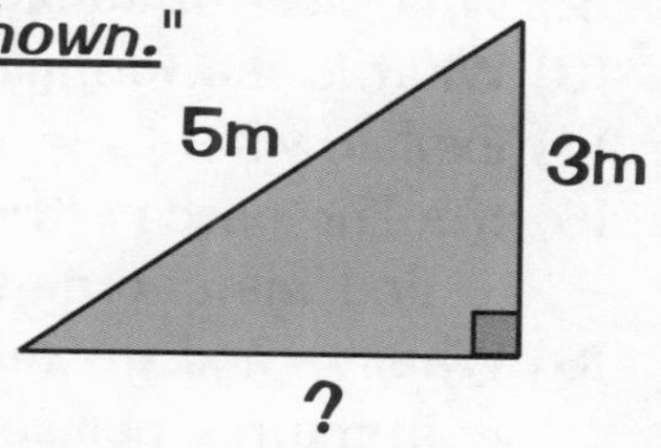

ANSWER: ❶ Square them: $5^2 = 25$, $3^2 = 9$
❷ You want to find a shorter side, so SUBTRACT: $25 - 9 = 16$
❸ Square root: $\sqrt{16} = 4$
So the missing side = 4m

(You should always ask yourself: "Is it a *sensible answer*?" — in this case you can say "YES, because it's shorter than 5m, as it should be since 5m is the longest side, but not too much shorter")

Example 2: *"Find the length of the line segment shown."*

For coordinates, see P.58.

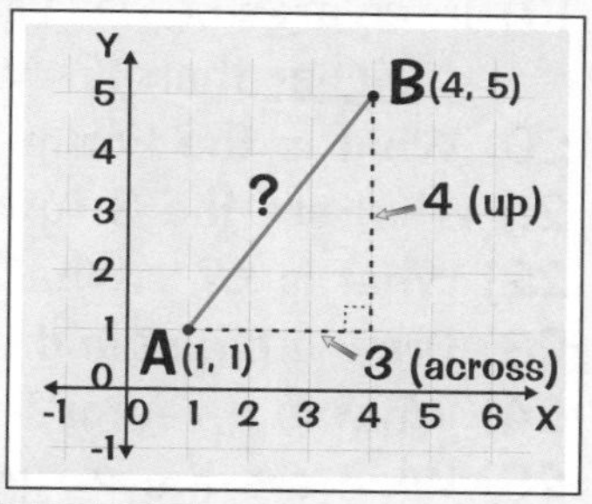

ANSWER: ❶ Work out how far across and up it is from A to B
❷ Treat this exactly like a normal triangle...
❸ Square them: $3^2 = 9$, $4^2 = 16$
❹ You want to find the longer side (the hypotenuse), so ADD: $9 + 16 = 25$
❺ Square root: $\sqrt{25} = 5$
So the length of the line segment = 5 units

The Acid Test:

LEARN the 2 facts relating Pythag. with SIN, COS, TAN, and the 3 steps of the Pythag. method.

Now *turn over and write down what you've learned*.

1) Then apply the above method to find the missing side BC:
2) Another triangle has sides of 5 m, 12 m and 13 m. Is it a right-angled triangle? How do you know?

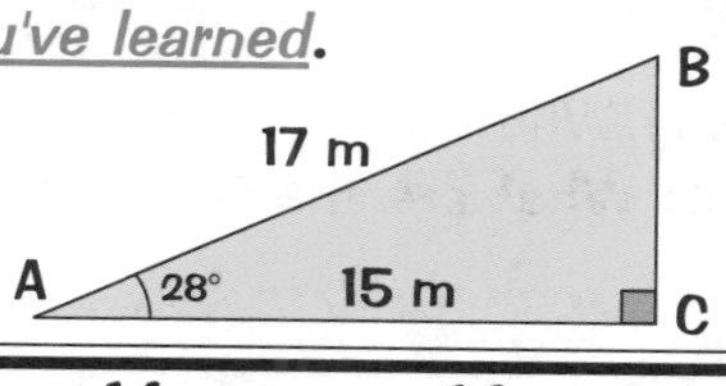

Revision Test for Module Five

Time to find out what you *don't* know and then learn it until you do. These questions follow the sequence of pages in Module Five, so you can easily look up anything you don't know — but give all the questions a go first.

Keep learning these basic facts until you know them

1) List the first ten terms in each of these sequences:
   a) Even numbers b) Odd numbers c) Powers of 2
   d) Powers of 10 e) Triangle numbers
2) Write down the 2 formulas for finding the nth term of a number pattern.
3) Cancel this equation down to its simplest form: $2(y+1) = \frac{3x((x-2)\times(12x^2+6))}{9x(x-2)}$
4) How exactly do you get solutions to a quadratic once you've factorised it?
5) List the 4 steps for solving an equation by trial and improvement.
6) What happens with units when you work out the speed from a travel graph?
7) What are the four inequality symbols and what do they mean?
8) Sketch a pair of x and y axes and show on it where the x-coordinates and the y-coordinates are positive and negative in the four different regions.
9) What does the graph of inverse proportion look like?
10) What sort of equation produces a bucket shaped graph?
11) What about an upside down bucket?
12) What sort of equation produces a graph with a wiggle in the middle?
13) What is the formula for gradient? How do you remember it?
14) Explain what "y = mx + c" means, including the significance of m and c.
15) If a line passes through the two points P(12, 34) and Q(4, 12), find the coordinates of the midpoint of the line segment, PQ.
16) What x- and y-axes would you need if the gradient was going to be equal to speed, in metres per second?
17) What axes would you need if the gradient was going to be the *rate of flow* of water, in litres per minute?
18) In relation to the four enlargements, what does TERRY stand for?
19) In enlargements, what is the effect (on the lengths of the sides) of a scale factor bigger than 1? What is the effect of a scale factor smaller than 1?
20) What is the Formula Triangle for enlargements?
21) What are the 3 types of symmetry called? Draw an example of each.
22) What is π? What are the two circle formulae? When do you use them?
23) Draw a circle and show on it: radius, diameter, arc, chord, tangent.
24) What is a vector? Give the 4 main examples.
25) What are the 4 types of vector notation? Illustrate with an example.
26) How do you decide which sides of a triangle are the adjacent, opposite and hypotenuse?
27) How do you enter SIN 45° into the calculator?
28) What button will you have to press to find angles from SIN θ, COS θ and TAN θ?
29) What is θ? What sort of shape is needed for trigonometry?
30) What is the formula for Pythagoras' Theorem?
31) What are the three steps of the easy method for doing Pythagoras?

Answers

Module One

P1 Probability: ¾ P3 Tree diagrams: 8/15 P6 Graphs and Charts: 2) Guinea Pigs 68°, Rabbits 60°, Ducks 104°, Stick insects 48° 3) That they are not related to each other in any way. i.e. no correlation. P7 Stem and Leaf Diagrams and Distribution: 1) Sample too small, motorways not representative of average motorist, only done at one time of day and in one place, not easy to get accurate age from registration letter. Better approach: A more detailed survey which deals with all the above problems — surveying people emerging from various Post Offices with new tax discs might be good. Stratified or quota sampling would be essential in choosing the Post Offices.
P8 Mean, Median, Mode and Range: First, do this: -14, -12, -5, -5, 0, 1, 3, 6, 7, 8, 10, 14, 18, 23, 25
Mean = 5.27, Median = 6, Mode = -5, Range = 39 P9 Time Series: 1) a) period = 4 months
b) Find the average of the readings from months 1-4, then the average from months 2-5, then from months 3-6, etc. (& you could plot these on a graph to see the trend.)

P10 Frequency Tables:

No. of Phones	0	1	2	3	4	5	6	TOTALS
Frequency	1	25	53	34	22	5	1	141
No. × Frequency	0	25	106	102	88	25	6	352

Mean = 2.5, Median = 2, Mode = 2, Range = 6

P11 Grouped Frequency Tables:

Length(cm)	15.5 —	16.5 —	17.5 —	18.5 — 19.5	TOTALS
Frequency	12	18	23	8	61
Mid-Interval Value	16	17	18	19	—
Freq × M I V	192	306	414	152	1064

Mean = 17.4, Modal Group = 17.5 — 18.5, Median ≈ 17.5

P12/13 Cumulative Frequency: Median = 58 kg, Lower Quartile = 53 kg, Upper Quartile = 62 kg, Inter-quartile range 9 kg

Weight (kg)	41 – 45	46 – 50	51 – 55	56 – 60	61 – 65	66 – 70	71 – 75
Frequency	2	7	17	25	19	8	2
Cum. Freq.	2	9	26	51	70	78	80

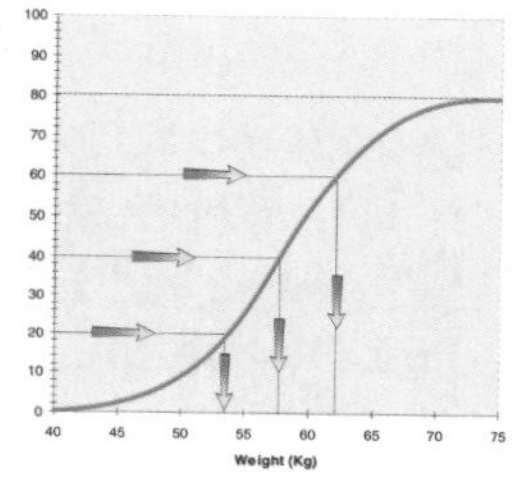

Module Three

P15 Multiples, Factors, Prime Factors: 1) 7,14,21,28,35,42,49,56,63,70 and 9,18,27,36,45,54,63,72,81,90 2) 1,2,3,4,6,9,12,18,36 and 1,2,3,4,6,7,12,14,21,28,42,84
3) 990 = 2×3×3×5×11, 160 = 2×2×2×2×2×5 P16 LCM and HCF: 1) 8,16,24,32,40,48,56,64,72,80 and 9,18,27,36,45,54,63,72,81,90 LCM = 72 2) 1,2,4,7,8,14,28,56 and 1,2,4,8,13,26,52,104
HCF = 8 3) 63 4) 12 P17 Prime numbers: 1) 2,3,5,7,11,13,17,19,23,29,31,37,41,43,47
2) 97, 101, 103, 107, 109 P18 Powers: 1) a) 3^8 b) 4 c) 8^{12} d) 1 e) 7^6 2) a) 5^{12} b) 36 or 6^2
c) 2^5 or 32 3) 6 P20 Square and Cube Roots: 1) a) 7.48 and -7.48 b) 7.66 c) 6.32 and -6.32
d) 20 2 a) g = 6 or -6 b) b = 4 c) r = 3 or -3 P22 Negative Numbers: 1a) +12 (Rule 1) b) -6 (Rule 2) c) -3 (Rule 1) 2a) 7 b) 5/4 3a) 120 b) 8 c) 50 P23 Fractions: See table below:

Fraction	Decimal	Percentage
1/5	0.2	20%
7/20	0.35	35%
9/20	0.45	45%
3/25	0.12	12%
1/8	0.125	12.5%
77/100	0.77	77%

P25 Fractions: 1 a) 3/8 b) 2 $^7/_{10}$ c) 11/15 d) x = 13
e) y = 1 f) 0.375 g) 35/1000 = 7/200 2 a) 8/15
b) 8/3 = 2 $^2/_3$ c) 1/2 d) 3/7 e) 84 f) 84 $^{12}/_{19}$
P27 Percentages: 1) Type 2, profit=£2, 40% 2) Type 1, £42.30 3) Type 3, £20,500 P28 Compound Growth and Decay: 1) 48 stick insects 2) 0.15m/s.
P30 Ratio: 1a) 5:7 b) 2:3 c) 3:5 2) 17½ bowls of porridge 3) £3500 : £2100 : £2800 P31 Conversion Factors: 1) 2,300m 2) £34 3) 3.2cm
P32 Proportion: 2) £8.05 P34 Standard Form: 1) 9.58×10^{15}, 1.8×10^{-4} 2) 2.7×10^4 3) 1.2×10^{10}
P35 Rounding Off: 1) 3.57 2) 0.05 3) 12.910 4) 3546.1 P36 Rounding Off: 1) a) 3.41
b) 1.05 c) 0.07 d) 3.60 2 a) 568 (Rule 2) b) 23400 (Rule 3) c) 0.0456 (Rules 1 and 3)
d) 0.909 (Rules 1 and 2) 3) 16 feet 6 in. to 17 feet 6 in.

P41 Calculator Buttons: 1) See P.39 2) [17] [x^2] [=] 3) [(–)] [5] [×] [(–)] [8] [=] or [5] [+/–] [×] [8] [+/–] [=]
4) See P.39 5) Fractions 6) [6] [x^y] [8] [=] 7) [6] [EXP] [8] [=] 8) DEG (or D)

Answers

Module Five

P43 Special Number Sequences: 1) a) EVENS: 2,4,6,8,10,12,14,16,18,20,22,24,26,28,30 b) ODDS: 1,3,5,7,9,11,13,15,17,19,21,23,25,27,29 c) POWERS OF 2: 2, 4, 8, 16, 32, 64, 128, 256, 512, 1024, 2048, 4096, 8192, 16384, 32768; POWERS OF 10: 10, 100, 1000, 10 000, 100 000, 1 000 000, 10 000 000, 100 000 000, 1 000 000 000, 10 000 000 000, 100 000 000 000, 1 000 000 000 000, 10 000 000 000 000, 100 000 000 000 000, 1 000 000 000 000 000 hmm... d) TRIANGLE Nos: 1,3,6,10,15,21,28,36,45,55,66,78,91,105,120 2) a) 56, 134, 156, 36, 64 b) 23, 45, 81, 25, 97, 125, 1 c) 64 d) 45, 36, 1 P44 Finding the nth Term: 1 a) 3n + 1 b) 5n – 2 c) $\frac{1}{2}n(n+1)$ d) $n^2 - 2n + 4$ P47 Basic Algebra: 1) a) 4x + y – 4 b) $4y^2 - 2k + 2$ c) 2x + 2 2) a) $6p^2q - 8pq^3$ b) $8g^2 + 16g - 10$ c) $16 - 24h + 9h^2$ 3) a) $7xy^2(2xy + 3 - 5x^2y^2)$ b) $6h^2j(2j^2 + h^2jk - 6hk)$ P48 Easy Equations: 1) x = 8 2) x = 7 P49 Solving Equations: a) x = 4 b) q = 32 c) p = 5.5 d) y= -2

P50 Substitution: 2) 25° C P51 Formulae: 1) $C = \frac{5}{9}(F - 32)$, $F = \frac{9}{5}C + 32$ 2) a) p = -4y/3

b) $p = \sqrt{\frac{y}{x^2 - 3}}$ P52 Quadratics: 1) a) X = -2 or -3 b) x = -6 or -2 c) x = 3 or -8 d) x = 7 or -1 P53 Trial and Improvement: 1) X = 1.6 P54 Simultaneous Equations: F = 3 G = -1 P55 Sim. Eq^{n}s With Graphs: 2) a) x=2, y=4 b) x=1½, y=3 P56 Solving Equations With Graphs: 1) x = 0.7 or 4.3 2) x=2.1 P57 Travel Graphs: 1) 0.5 km/h 2) Phew. Ask your teacher.

P58 Inequalities: 1) X ⩾ -2 2) -4, -3, -2 , -1, 0, 1
P59 Graphical Inequalities: 1) See graph:

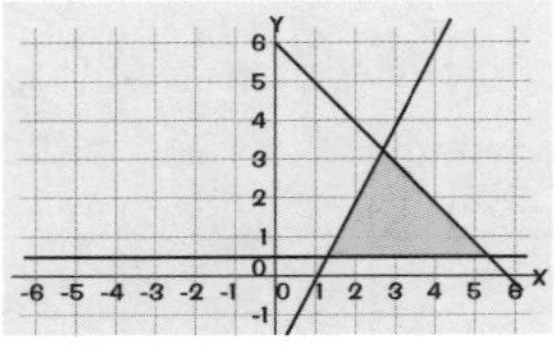

P60 X and Y Coordinates: 1) A(4,5) B(6,0) C(5,-5) D(0,-3) E(-5,-2) F(-4,0) G(-3,3) H(0,5)
P61 Easy Graphs You Should Know: 1) a) y = x b) y = –x c) y = 2 d) y = ½x 2)

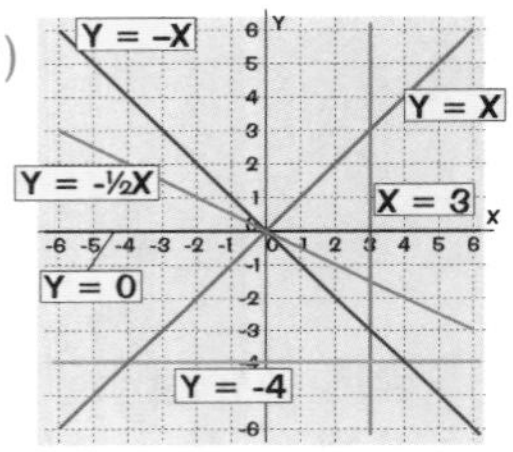

P64 Finding the Gradient of a Line: 1) -3/2
P65 Plotting S/L Graphs:
P66 Plotting Straight Line Graphs:

1) 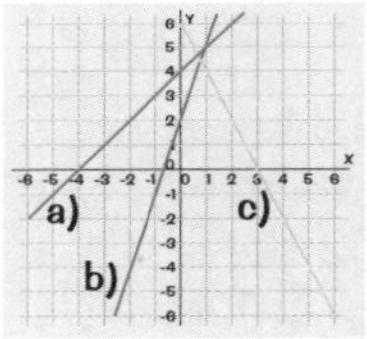

1) 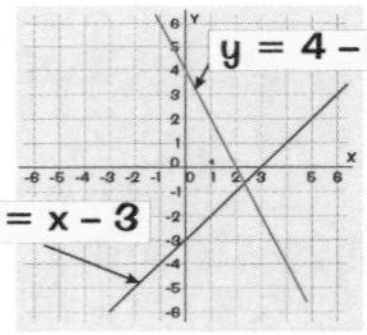

2) 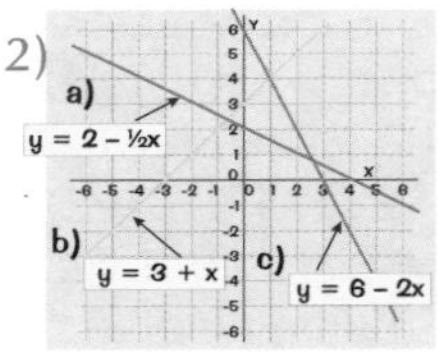

3) N = (10, 7.5)

P68 Typical Graph Questions:

1)

x	-2	-1	0	1	2	3	4	5	6
y	15	8	3	0	-1	0	3	8	15

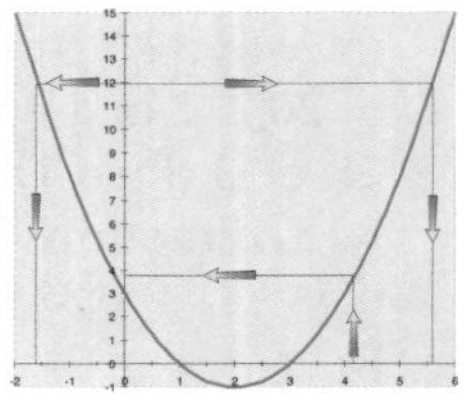

2) Y = 3.8, X = -1.6 and 5.6 3) Miles per Gallon, ie. fuel consumption

P69 Transformations: A→B, Rotation of 90° clockwise about the origin.

B→C, Reflection in the line Y = X C→A, Reflection in the Y-axis. A→D, Translation of $\binom{-9}{-7}$

P70 Combinations of Transformations: 1) C→D, Reflection in the Y-axis, and an enlargement SF 2, centre the origin D→C, Reflection in the Y-axis, and an enlargement SF ½, centre the origin.
2) A'→B, Rotation of 180° clockwise or anticlockwise about the point (0,3). P73 Symmetry:

H : 2 lines of symmetry, Rot^{nl}. symmetry Order 2,
E : 1 line of symmetry, no Rotational symmetry,
M : 1 line of symmetry, no Rotational symmetry,
S : 0 lines of symmetry, Rot^{nl}. symmetry Order 2,
N: 0 lines of symmetry, Rot^{nl}. symmetry Order 2
Y: 1 line of symmetry, no Rot^{nl}. symmetry
O: 2 lines of symmetry, Rot^{nl}. symmetry Order 2
T: 1 line of symmetry, no Rot^{nl}. symmetry

Answers

P76 Circle Questions: 1) Area = 153.9cm² Circumference = 44.0 cm 2) A = 113.0m², C = 37.7m
P77 Perimeters and Areas: 2) Perimeter = 49.7cm Area = 129.3cm² P78 Volume or Capacity:
a) Trapezoidal Prism, V = 148.5 cm³ b) Cylinder, V = 0.70 m³ P79 Solids and Nets: 1) 128.8cm²
2) 294cm² 3) 174cm² 4) 96cm² P81 Geometry: 1) z = 65° 2) 360° 3) 540°
4) 120° and 60° all round (see below) P84 Bearings: 1) 118° 2) 298° P86 Projections, Congruence and Similarity: 1) See P.86 and check it looks right. 2) a) i, ii and iv are similar. b) i and ii are congruent.
P88 Trigonometry: 1) X = 26.5m 2) 23.6° 3) 32.60° (both)
P89 Pythagoras: 1) BC = 8m, 2) 5m, 12m, 13m is a right angled triangle because $a^2 + b^2 = h^2$ *works.*

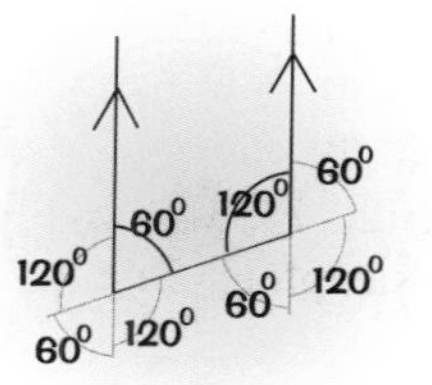

Index

Index

MAIR41